Advanced Ethics
for Addiction
Professionals

Michael J. Taleff, PhD, CSAC, MAC has worked in the alcohol and other drug field for over thirty-five years, and teaches substance abuse courses at Leeward Community College in Hawaii. He was the first editor of the *Journal of Teaching in the Addictions*. He has published some 100 articles that address various aspects of addictions studies education. He has also published several books including *A Handbook to Assess and Treat Resistance in Chemical Dependency, Critical Thinking for Addiction Professionals*, and writes a bi-monthly column for *Counselor Magazine*. He served on the editorial board of *The Journal of Counseling and Development*, and the *Journal of Offenders and Addiction Counseling*. Presently, he is on the editorial board of *The Counselor*. Dr. Taleff served two terms as president of the *International Coalition of Addiction Studies Educators*, and presents widely on state-of-the-art addiction research, critical thinking, and advanced ethics.

Advanced Ethics for Addiction Professionals

MICHAEL J. TALEFF, PhD, CSAC, MAC

SPRINGER PUBLISHING COMPANY

New York

Springer Publishing Company, LLC
11 West 42nd Street
New York, NY 10036
www.springerpub.com

Acquisitions Editor: Jennifer Perillo
Project Manager: Mark Frazier
Cover Design: David Levy
Composition: Apex CoVantage, LLC

E-book ISBN: 978-0-8261-2459-3

09 10 11 12/ 5 4 3 2 1

The author and the publisher of this Work have made every effort to use sources believed to be reliable to provide information that is accurate and compatible with the standards generally accepted at the time of publication. Because medical science is continually advancing, our knowledge base continues to expand. Therefore, as new information becomes available, changes in procedures become necessary. We recommend that the reader always consult current research and specific institutional policies before performing any clinical procedure. The author and publisher shall not be liable for any special, consequential, or exemplary damages resulting, in whole or in part, from the readers' use of, or reliance on, the information contained in this book. The publisher has no responsibility for the persistence or accuracy of URLs for external or third-party Internet Web sites referred to in this publication and does not guarantee that any content on such Web sites is, or will remain, accurate or appropriate.

Library of Congress Cataloging-in-Publication Data

Taleff, Michael J.
    Advanced ethics for addiction professionals / Michael J. Taleff.
      p. ; cm.
    Includes bibliographical references and index.
    ISBN 978-0-8261-2458-6 (alk. paper)
  1. Drug abuse counselors—Professional ethics.   I. Title.
    [DNLM: 1. Behavior, Addictive—therapy.   2. Counseling—ethics.
  3. Decision Making—ethics.   WM 62 T143a 2010]
    HV5275.T25 2010
    174'.296860651—dc22   2009030555

Printed in the United States of America by Hamilton Printing.

For my children, Stephanie and Joseph.

Contents

Preface

This book idea grew out of a series of advanced ethics workshops I presently conduct for addiction counselors. To retain certification, counselors always need a certain number of continuing credit hours between certification periods. Each certification period generally extends for 2 years. Out of the total hours required, 6 hours have to be in the area of ethics.

Yet there is a little problem with the ethics requirement. Every 2 years, presenters are offered basically the same ethics workshop over and over. After sitting through the same workshop a few times, participants desire something a little different. An idea occurred to me that the addiction field could use something new and innovative to fill that desire. The idea coincided with Springer Publishing Company's offer to publish my book, *Critical Thinking for Addiction Professionals*. It occurred to me that one could combine ethics with critical thinking. This way, participants could expand their ethics knowledge beyond the same old set of dos and don'ts so often presented in traditional ethics workshops and books. The most intriguing possibly of such a combination was to get an audience to seriously think about the complicated ethical problems facing our field. The ultimate goal was to ponder addiction ethics and to make it interesting and challenging. Hence, the advanced ethics for substance abuse counselors workshop was born.

A pivotal goal of this workshop has been to make sure participants leave the presentation with more questions than answers. Hopefully this creates a thinking itch that needs to be scratched by forcing participants to closely examine how and why they come to their ethical decisions rather than mindlessly spouting ethical pronouncements minus the deliberation. This is an important purpose of both the workshop and this book.

The first time I offered the workshop, it was surprisingly successful, and the attendance has remained strong for the last few years. Between each presentation, I tweak the workshop slightly. This is due to the spirited discussions of the workshop that force me to rethink a position, and also to my constant reading. Both bring something fresh to each new workshop presentation. In this manner, the workshops do not become stale. The presentations have evolved and even include elements of philosophy, which I personally think the addiction field could use.

The next logical step was to extend this workshop to a book. I hope this volume captures the spirit and utility of the workshops and encourages readers to think more fully about their own ethical decision-making process.

Acknowledgments

Books rarely come about without the influence and advice of others. Several people were instrumental in the creation of this one. First, I wish to thank Jennifer Perillo at Springer Publishing Company for approaching me with an idea for a book. Second, I wish to thank Chris Brown and Ralph Marsh from the Hawaii Alcohol and Drug Abuse Division for initially allowing me to present the idea for an advanced ethics workshop. I have appreciated the support throughout the years. Third, I wish to thank the many participants of the workshop and my students. Our sometimes spirited but thoughtful interactions pressed me to think and to make improvements to the workshop, and the many suggestions eventually ended up in this book.

Advanced Ethics
for Addiction
Professionals

The Foundation: A Thinking Way to Approach Addiction Ethics

1   Introduction to Ethical Thinking

Today professionals working in the addiction field face ever-increasing and complex ethical problems. The intensity of such issues demands meaningful moral reasoning on how to address them. Professionals do not need a simple laundry list of "don't do this" and "don't do that," yet many of the existing books on the subject typically follow this format. However, that is not the only way to teach ethics these days. We need to move on a bit, and offer addiction professionals the ability to really reflect on ethical decisions. Therefore, the emphasis in this book is on *how* to make those difficult ethical decisions.

It is also past time for something really fresh in addiction ethics. This book is remarkably different in that it will not only press you to think and process addiction ethics issues, but throughout the book it will press you to examine *yourself*. Not in terms of how ethical you are, but in terms of how well you ethically think.

Addiction counselors are busy and need books that are easy to read with a friendly format. Thus, the jargon often found in traditional ethics books is kept to a minimum here. In addition, there are copious diagrams to assist understanding the more challenging ideas. This should be an inviting format for readers. Hopefully, it will give the book a comfort element that stays clear of the long and the laborious.

Part of the book will ask the reader to examine ethical dilemmas outside the realm of addiction issues (e.g., death penalty and abortion, among others). The reason or premise is that if one can clearly engage such heady issues thoughtfully, then surely one can engage addiction ethics.

After conducting advanced ethics for addiction counselors workshops for years, and writing this book, I realized that much of this journey had an element of self-discovery. As an illustration, I was not sure of the ethical foundations I often relied on to make my judgments. I noted that many people in my audience had the same problem. But now readers have an opportunity to find what ethical stance they really favor and rely on for many of the ethical judgments that need to be made. We rarely engage at this level of moral self-exploration. It seems exciting that you have the potential by the end of the book to discover the ethical foundations to which you most gravitate. This should prove interesting especially in those cases where readers might have never felt they had an ethical position in the first place.

While I don't have a formal education in philosophy, over the years I have read a multitude of books in the area, and I still continually read philosophy and critical thinking material. After reading all those books I have observed that while the insights gained from philosophy are interesting, they continue to be nebulous, and often difficult. Many philosophy books, in particular, have a bad habit of spinning off into esoteric corners of thought. A big problem with such books is that they are written by philosophers who are talking to their specialized peers. The result is that they resort to esoteric language to explain something like ethics, and end up using language that is not translatable to the common person (including me). Being in the addiction field as long as I have, I know this level of reading is not going to attract or encourage addiction counselors to engage complex ethical questions.

What you get in this book is a view of ethics from someone who is at heart an addiction counselor but has read a ton of philosophy. The intent is to make difficult thought more palatable and down-to-earth without needing a philosophy degree. Thus, philosophers will have difficultly with this book. Hopefully, my colleagues who work in the trenches every day won't.

I should make clear that this not a comparative ethics book. That is not the intention. Yet the intent is to sting readers to think for themselves (Woodhouse, 1994). Hopefully this book will encourage a quest or journey to find answers. However, quests usually come with a price—you have to do a little work. And as I state in my advanced ethics workshops, I frankly want to piss off the reader to some extent. Why? People who are a little angry are more prone to investigate, even read, with the hope they can formulate better responses to some of the issues that come up.

I would hope there is a hint of originality to this book. Unlike most addiction ethics books, this one has a guiding theme, one that hopefully forces you to self-examine your moral and ethical positions. Not your personal ethics, mind you, but the positions by which you judge those and other's ethics. In other words, the book is meant to push the reader a little deeper in the understanding of addiction-oriented ethics if not forward in professional development. It attempts to teach ethics without indoctrination (Paul, 1993). By comparison, consider that we insist our clients self-examine in order to better understand themselves. Hence, a moral/ethical self-examination on your part may lobby you to better understand who you are. That effort may force you to treat your clients with all the ethical and moral skill you can muster. If that doesn't float your boat, consider this book a journey where you enter as you are now and come out the other end different. Better, but different. A quest.

For those budding critics looking for an all-encompassing tome, this is not that book. There are a number of such existing books on the market. They sport an abundant number of case examples, lists of ethical codes, and banks of study questions. I encourage the eager reader to seek them out.

JUDGING

This book encourages you to judge. No! That's not quite right, it *insists* you judge. Granted, this isn't a very popular idea in these highly tolerant and so-called politically correct days. Yet the push behind this drive comes from several observations that worry me. One involves watching addiction professionals unable to make clear statements on the complex ethical situation and dilemmas they face. When presented with such ethical problems, some addiction professionals shrug their shoulders in bewilderment and continue their professional lives as if the ethical situations in questions have no bearing or relevance to them. More troubling are the pithy responses often made to complex addiction ethical problems, or worse, responses made with flawed thought or dogma. Sadly, whether the pompous response is made from the left or right, it is often made without much extra thought.

The second troubling observation is of addiction professionals who opt out of judging altogether because they think that to judge is somehow bad. What often sometimes drives an "I don't judge others" position is the rush to be overly tolerant. Many in our field are trying to be inclusive and open-minded, and that is a worthy ideal. And while it would be difficult to argue against tolerance, it is easy to argue against excessive tolerance (Shermer, 2004). Essentially, anything taken to extremes is generally not a healthy position. Such is the case for excessive tolerance. For our purposes, that is a position that allows an anything goes attitude. Moreover, these nonjudgers claim no one has the right to make a judgment about anything, because all people are entitled to their opinions, and to run their lives as they please. Translated, it essentially says all moral positions are valid. This has a number of problems—big problems. For one, such a position prohibits one from ever making a judgment about any moral or ethical issue, including addiction ethics. Think about it: our clients, colleagues, and administrators would have free reign to morally do as they please under the guise of being excessively tolerant, because whatever position they took to come to such a position would be tolerated. The other major problem with this stance is that one cannot have a moral standard with excessive tolerance. Anything goes means anything goes. Pardon my judgment, but anything goes leaves open some pretty ugly things to pass by that need thought and judgment. Anything goes is not morality.

Finally, what often happens with the no-judge position is that people take advantage of it. The no-judge position also serves as a safety zone or cushion where people appear to be tolerant but wish not to upset anyone or any position and hence stand for very little (Shermer, 2004). And even a notable ethicist such as MacKinnon (2004) notes that judgment needs moral courage. Consider moral courage to be a willingness to face and assess moral ideas and beliefs fairly regardless of our strong reaction to them (Paul, 1993).

On the other hand, according to Shermer, some folks would oppose judgment based on the teachings of sacred books—for example, the biblical maxim "judge not lest you be judged." A closer examination of this oft-used statement against judging is not, however, to be considered a statement against all moral judgments. It is not advocating giving a blank check to all moral acts. A close reading of Matthew 7:1–5 warns instead not to become self-righteous in your judgment or rush to judgment. It warns against becoming smug or becoming a hypocrite in judging others when the judger is lacking in virtue him or herself. That is the same warning here. Don't rush to judgment. But, when you do judge, when you need to judge, judge well, which happens to be the really big theme of this book.

Finally, I find myself upset, as is Brown (1996), with those who switch from passionate certainty to radical doubt without as much as a blink of an eye, or without considering how they make such oscillations of thought without accounting for them. All these listed problems are nonproductive routes to a critical examination of today's multifaceted addiction ethics problems.

You are therefore encouraged to take a position on things, especially on addiction ethics issues. Take note that it is judging badly that may well be at the core of many problems and biases today. You are therefore asked to judge, but to do it well.

Example: Judge an Evolving Ethical Situation

Instructions

You are to judge (yes, judge) each bulleted statement separately. Then as the story evolves, judge each subsequent statement. Observe if your judgments change. If they do, ask yourself why, and then proceed to the end bullet.

- You find out that a colleague (Willy) had a boundary crossing relationship with his client (Rhonda). Rhonda was paid to clean Willy's house.

Now Stop and Judge

- Now, you find out the money helped Rhonda, who really needed the funds.

Stop and Judge

- The alleged event took place several months ago.

Stop and Judge

- Willy's supervisor finds out what happened, and Willy faces disciplinary action.

Stop and Judge

- Following the reprimand, Willy expresses guilt and regret.

Stop and Judge

- Willy tells you that the reprimand will be two days without pay. He tells you this will be a hardship in terms of paying bills and providing for his family.

Stop and Judge

- You note that Willy is always on time, gets his work done, and is well liked by his clients.

Stop and Judge

- Following the reprimand, Willy discloses that two similar events took place with Rhonda.

Stop and Judge

- Willy then discloses that he did all this because his sibling who is exactly the same age has similar problems as Rhonda but hasn't responded to treatment. Willy has been feeling helpless, and wanted to go above and beyond with his client.

Now that you know all the parameters of this situation, ethically what would you do? You could go for the pithy responses of "I think I will punt on this one," "I'll just trust my gut," or "Just keep it simple," among others. Those do not seem adequate to the task placed before us. Small questions might guide you to needed resources, and that would be a start. Big questions would press you to sift out what was right and wrong in each of the bullets listed. To really answer this ethical situation fully, you and I need the assistance of extraordinary thinking processes, which is what this book is all about. But let's first get to the type of questions just posed.

Big and Small Questions

Turnbull (1998) points out that there are two kinds of questions—big and small. Granted, that doesn't sound very scientific, but it is appropriate for our purposes. The small questions, or conventional kinds of questions, typically generate commonsense answers. What will I have for breakfast? What is that best way to get to a critical thinking workshop? Or even: What might be a good video to show to a group of incarcerated inmates with addiction problems?

But then we have the big questions. Appiah (2003) speaks of big questions as *first-order* moral questions because they ask about giant issues like what is right and wrong, what is good and bad. Because of their scale and scope, commonsense responses or pithy responses will just not do. Such big questions require a little extra thought and consideration. For example, how does one give a pithy answer to the complex ethical question of an evolving boundary crossing situation as illustrated previously?

A FEW GROUND RULES

The press to make judgments comes partly from years of research cited by the renowned neurobiologist Gazzaniga (2005). That research revealed that our brain evolved to make decisions. It is a decision-making device. Hence, if we are a decision-making species, all the more reason to make the best decisions possible when faced with complex ethical predicaments.

Now that we know that our brains are decision-making devices, we need to define a few things up front because there will always be those individuals who do not make good decisions. They will use bad decision-making processes or will draw on all kinds of bad thinking processes. They will jump to conclusions concerning addiction ethics decisions. They might even accuse this book of things it does not state. So this brings us to a few rules concerning ethical disagreements. One has to do with the lost art of argument or criticism versus the trendy jump to judge and condemn people and beliefs.

Judging Versus Criticism and Condemnation

True criticism is an honest, malice-free assessment of an idea or an action. In our case, you are encouraged to criticize your ethical judgments and those made by colleagues and even the so-called experts. If done well, the criticism will be thorough and reasonable. It will point out strengths and weaknesses. Done in the right spirit, it is a positive undertaking that can produce greater understanding for the sake of wisdom and virtue. While it doesn't feel good to get criticism, it is beneficial, and if taken gracefully, it allows us to improve and become better at this judging thing.

Condemnation and demonizing, on the other hand, go beyond criticism because they are never fair, always negative, and always judgmental. They refer mostly to weakness and are directed at a person, a person's character, a community, or a culture. They are meant to do harm, period (Brown, 2001; Tannan, 1998). You are asked to avoid condemnation and especially avoid demonizing others.

Discussion and Argument With an Agenda

Right behind the ideas of criticism and condemnation are the issues of discussion and argument with an agenda attached. With discussion, we deliberate for the sake of coming to a truth. If there is to be confrontation (and often there is in addiction ethics), it is orderly with an added element of a willingness to learn. It involves the presentation of evidence and solid reasoning, with a goal of understanding.

Generally, argument as the philosophers discuss it is very close to the idea of discussion. However, an argument with an agenda is one where we abandon the pursuit of truth for that of triumph. The agenda presses you to fight for personal victory. An agenda-tainted argument comes with an element of bad faith, because we are not honestly pursuing truth together. Simply, those who do this type of arguing just want their position to be right and you to be wrong. Arguments with an agenda displace fruitful discussions and replace it with accusations and power manipulations (Brown, 2001). You are asked to avoid argument with an agenda.

POSITIONS, STANDS, AND FOUNDATIONS

What's your position on using clients in your program to wash your personal car? If you favor such a position, on what set of premises do you make such a stand? That means, what reasons do you have to support and defend this argument? This type of argument is what we refer to as a position, stand, or foundation. Whether you know it or not, you and I have a ton of such positions in our heads. What we will attempt here is to make you more aware of your particular positions, stands, and foundations.

To press this point, consider the following questions seriously. For what would you be willing to give your life? What reasons would you give to make the ultimate sacrifice?

Notice that both questions require positions, stands, and foundations. "I would be willing to sacrifice my life for my children," is a stand. "Why? Because I love them and am willing to do anything to see them happy and secure." This belief is a central belief. As this has a core position within it (make them happy and secure), it is a foundation.

As stated, we all have these positions. You carry them around all the time, every day. Most of the time, these positions are invisible unless they are provoked. In a manner of speaking, you rest or sit on these positions. You probably sit on one or two main foundations and usually a set of lesser stances (see Figure 1.1). They, in a lot of ways, determine who you are, and how you think, and, yes, how you judge.

If it hasn't already happened to you yet, one day you will have to defend one of your addiction ethics positions. Someone, somewhere is going to come after one of your cherished positions, stands, or foundational beliefs and challenge it. He or she is going to confront what you believe is ethical, and in what you have ethical faith. Obviously, the more stable, better your foundation, the better the chance to withstand the challenge.

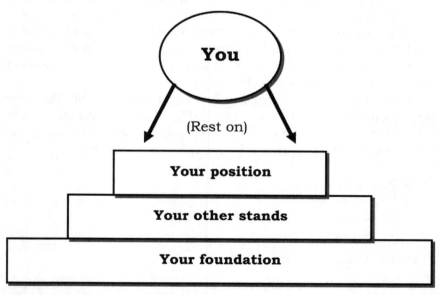

Figure 1.1 Positions, stands, and foundations.

So one of the goals of this book is to assess how true or genuine your ethical positions, stands, and foundations really are. We will also delve a bit into the epistemology of the ethics realm (Curtler, 2004).

GAINING ETHICAL PERSPECTIVE

We start this section by encouraging you to step as far back from ethics as you can get. The idea is to get what is called the *ethical perspective* or a distanced view (Curtler, 2004). People do not normally do this. They often stand too close to their ethical position to really know what the big ethical picture looks like. This causes a constricted or sometimes myopic view of things. By analogy, this would be like only seeing your home town and believing that other parts of the world live and work in the same way. However, recall your first airline flight and how you felt watching the earth from 35,000 feet or how you felt sitting on a high cliff overlooking the Grand Canyon or the Smoky Mountains. This grand view allows the big picture of our world to settle in. That kind of spacious view is encouraged here.

The point is to see the really big picture of ethics and then slowly move in for a close-up. Along the way, you hopefully will begin to see where your ethics seem to fit. Another reason for seeking this perspective is that you may see things you never saw before, which is a nice way of saying that you may find some of your biases and prejudices. And as much as you may think your favorite view of morality is a good one—and it may be—it may also blind you to other points of view. Hence, another reason to push for this perspective thing.

To get started on this little trip, let's begin with, arguably, the three big ways to think about ethics (Law, 2007). This formulation is really helpful in terms of seeing ethics in an orderly way and taking the grand perspective mentioned previously. The three big views are:

- Practical ethics
- Normative ethics
- Metaethics

Practical Ethics

Practical or descriptive ethics are what most of us associate with ethics. For example, have you ever tried to make a point for or against a certain behavior? Say, for instance, that a colleague has begun to spend more and more time using a work computer for personal purposes. This obviously takes time away from her work. Let's add that some clients have begun to complain that they are not getting time to discuss recovery issues with this colleague. You approach this individual and state your case that all this personal computer time is robbing clients of therapy. You state an ethical claim, which happens to be that you feel your colleague's behavior is wrong. Well, if you ever did something like this, you have engaged in practical ethics. And the examples of practical ethics seem to be limitless.

While there are some general guidelines to practical ethics such as Johnson and Ridley (2008), Pope and Vasquez (2007), and Kidder (2003), among others, most folks facing an ethical dilemma only have a hazy sense of consciously judging what's right or wrong. More often than not, they have a particular, often strong, feeling about it. It is from those intangible judgment standards and feelings that we typically pronounce an action right or wrong.

Notice the term "intangible" was just used. Keep in mind you are now looking out over this grand landscape of ethics, which includes your personal ethics. Now, here is a significant question that directs your attention to a very important point. Is there any bias or favoritism in that intangible ethical stance of yours?

Keep the question and possible answer in the back of your mind as we proceed to the next big ethical stance.

Normative Ethics

It is at *normative ethics* that we begin to use a measure or ruler of some kind from which to gauge the rightness or wrongness of an action. Normative ethics tells you what you should do (Law, 2007). And it provides a set of rulers to do just that. Using the preceding example, an ethical judgment is made from an established ethical position, not from a hazy sense of right or wrong. For example, you might judge the colleague's personal use of her work computer by stating, "The state code of ethics, or some dead philosopher, says you should not spend excess time on that computer because it is wrong."

Now there are three big theories (and a number of minor theories to be touched on later) listed under normative ethics: utilitarianism, deontology, and virtue ethics (Law, 2007). Each, in its own way, attempts to gauge which actions are right and which are wrong. We will take a closer

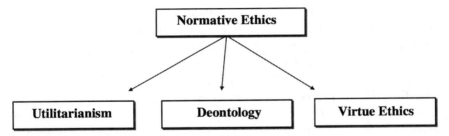

Figure 1.2 Normative ethics.

look at each of these in chapter 5. But for the time being, just know that they are specific methods under the broad heading of normative ethics (See Figure 1.2).

Metaethics

Finally, from the big three, let's take a look at *metaethics*. This is the fun part, because you now get to reflect and critically evaluate your personal ethics, along with all those normative ethical stands that have come down through the ages. That is what metaethics is about, studying the very ideas of right and wrong (Law, 2007). *Meta* is a Greek term meaning above, beyond, or stretching across (Baggini & Fosl, 2007). This meta view is much like the grand ethical perspective noted previously.

Not that we are going to get deeply into metaethics, but some of the more contentious issues it dares to address are things like the following (Baggini & Fosl, 2007):

- Are there such things as moral facts?
- No moral truths can be known.
- Moral truths can be known, and they are either true or false.
- Moral judgments are essentially subjective.

Heady stuff. And while we will touch on some of this, the implications are way beyond the scope of this book. I just wanted to give you an idea of what metaethics is all about.

Summing up, Figure 1.3 gives you a broad picture of the ethical world.

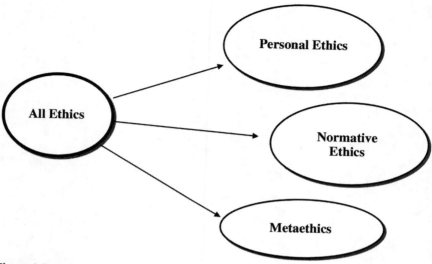

Figure 1.3 Ethics: The big picture.

THE LEAST YOU NEED TO KNOW

- Judge, but do it well.
- There are two types of ethical questions—small and big.
- The ground rules for ethical arguments: strive for criticism and discussion; avoid condemnation and arguing with an agenda.
- We all have moral and ethical positions, stands, and foundations.
- Gain ethical perspective.
- The three ethical perspectives include personal ethics, normative ethics, and metaethics.

2

Beyond Ordinary Ethics: Why and How

There are regrettably too few books on addiction ethics. The few that exist set out to tell you what is right and wrong, and they do all the labor for you. Generally, that's not a bad approach. In fact, it is a very good way to write a book. Tomes of this nature are typically manuals of how to judge ethically and how to behave professionally. Many folks in our field need that because they are either a little short on an internal moral compass or they need a refresher course on what to do and what not to do in their daily work.

For example, addiction counselors need guidance around certain behaviors such as the rule against sleeping with clients. Now ask a sample of addiction counselors why we should not do such a thing, and often you get weak answers like, "It's wrong," "You should not take advantage of clients," "It betrays trust," or "That's what I was taught in my workshop class." Frequently, the same frail answers are often given for why addiction counselors should not breach confidentiality laws, or not gouge insurance companies with excessive or bogus charges: "Because it's wrong," "It betrays trust," "My state code of ethics prohibits that." These simple answers may reveal lazy thinking. And in these ethically complex days, lethargic thinking will produce anemic answers. That will no longer do.

This book presses you not to just follow the so-called experts or to parrot someone else's set of ethics. This book presses you to dig deep into why you ethically act and judge the way you do. When experts, your supervisor, colleagues, and maybe your own inner voice tell you that sleeping with a client is wrong, or breaching confidentiality is wrong, generally that's the end of the thinking process. While it sounds dumb, one has to press the question—*why* is it wrong? I mean really get a good handle on why such things are wrong. That means establishing solid reasons, plus having a logic system well rooted in your mind. Not because some expert, code, or book said so.

For instance, many typical addiction ethics books tell you to abide by the principles of beneficence and nonmaleficence. But why would you abide by these principles? Because someone told you that it was the right thing to do? Because you think it is a good idea? Well, those thoughts represent rudimentary thinking, but not to the level outlined in this book. This book wants to press you to really figure out *why* you came to the conclusions you came to. It will push you to come up with your own answers, but more importantly, it will push you to come up with good solid reasons for the answers.

Let's make it very clear that this book is not about making you into a moralizer, or someone who seeks to impose how one should live or behave on others (Grayling, 2002). Instead, the only thing this book will insist on is clear thought. It encourages you to figure out why certain human behaviors are considered unethical. In a nutshell, it presses you to improve your way of thinking, which will in turn improve your reasoned beliefs, which will in turn allow you to make levelheaded and appropriate ethical actions. Finally, it presses you to *take a stand*, even though you may not want to (see Figure 2.1).

This process is akin to a self-exploration of sorts. As addiction counselors, we constantly urge our clients to self-explore in the hopes of coming to a better understanding of themselves. There is no difference here, but the focus is on understanding that part of you that has to do with morals and ethics. I do not have data on this, but I would assume most addiction professionals don't do this. And while we certainly study hard to understand the latest counseling theories, or the latest theories of addiction onset and maintenance, rarely do we study our own ethics.

Finally, and this is very important, you do not want to simply become skilled in tearing other people's ethical decisions apart. That's actually rather easy to do. You need to be able to make well-reasoned decisions of your own (Thomson, 1999).

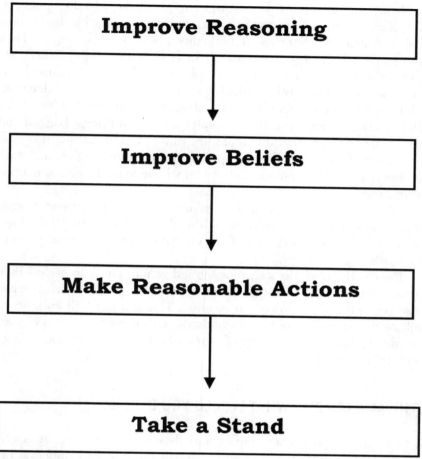

Figure 2.1 Take a stand.

We will come back to this important point shortly.

We are now approaching the realm of advanced ethics or thinking ethics. This realm needs a different—even special—way of thinking. For example, say you know that one of your colleagues, a very close friend and confidant, tells you she is having an affair with another staff member and often they manage to spend secret time in your friend's office. If the question you ask yourself shifts from "What shall I do?" to "What *should* I do?" then you have entered the realm of ethical and moral reasoning (Thomson, 1999).

Notice immediately that the question "What should I do?" puts you in a dilemma. Should you act or not, and if you do, what is the best course of action? Dilemmas are not a nice place to be. Never are. They are two equally unfavorable alternatives (Johnson & Ridley, 2008). Yet being in such places forces you to employ more thought than usual and use an assorted set of other thinking skills to come to a good decision. While a dilemma may feel uncomfortable, one might say that being in a dilemma builds character. In the greater scheme of things, Baggini and Fosl (2003) indicate that dilemmas are vital to the forward and overall movement of thought and philosophy. Often a dilemma will reveal stark choices that have to be made and will impel one to investigate situations more closely.

While some may argue against taking a stand, you are encouraged to just the opposite. Consider how difficult it would be to conduct addiction ethics business devoid of any ethical judgment process or set of standards to guide us.

Finally, the book does have one grand goal in mind: to no less than introduce the reader to wonderful ideas and thoughts by which you can raise your ethical expertise and acumen. This practice will end, hopefully, with a strong set of moral standards. This should be a sign of your knowledge and internalization of moral norms and conventions (Tangney, Stueing, & Mashek, 2007).

ETHICAL EXAMPLE: WHAT WOULD YOU DECIDE?

Let's begin by posing a complex and thorny ethical issue. It is one that defies a simple solution and requires thought and deliberation. You are asked to mull over your ethical judgment and then to respond with what you presently have in your repertoire of ethical solutions. Ask yourself what decision you would make and, most importantly, ask what your reasons are for your decision. Try to hold your decision in mind, plus the reasons behind it. We will revisit them at the end of the book.

A few years ago, Fox News (2007) reported that a woman living in Michigan was charged with attempted manslaughter when her 5-month-old daughter died after breast-feeding. The women had been using cocaine for 2 to 3 days before the feeding. A medical examiner determined that the young child died of cocaine intoxication. The mother pleaded guilty to attempted manslaughter and received 9 months in jail.

The judge in the case also ordered the mother to pay court costs of $900 and serve 18 months of probation.

In your opinion, was this the best ethical thing to do to this mother? Build a case for your judgment.

THE FULL-SCALE VIEW: A DISTINCTION BETWEEN ETHICS AND MORALITY

We now need to work on our perspective, which means stepping back a bit to get the full view of ethics and morality. Let's start with the core concepts of ethics and morality. Depending on whom you read or talk to, some believe there is a discernable difference between ethics and morality. Seeing a difference may trigger a view to a bigger picture of things.

For example, according to Steward and Blocker (1982), ethics is a set of investigating principles that govern human actions in terms of goodness, badness, rightness, and wrongness. Ethics is about discovering or creating principles that should govern human conduct. Ethics is trying to discern right from wrong, or the investigation of morality (Johnson & Ridley, 2008). Think of it more as a discipline or the study of our values and how we live our lives. Simply, ethics is the study of right and wrong thought and behavior (Shermer, 2004).

Morality, on the other hand, is more basic, perhaps more profound. It engages right and wrong behavior (Shermer, 2004). It also involves the quality of being in accord with the standards and rules of good conduct (Solomon, 1993). With morality, you are not allowed the opportunity to distance yourself and study issues as you would a dissected frog. With morality, you have to live the rules. If done well, morality dignifies and elevates (Haidt, 2003).

One way to understand this view is to envision ethics as talking the talk, and morality as walking the walk.

THE FULL-SCALE VIEW: BIG ETHICAL QUESTIONS

In line with our wide view of addiction ethics is Christian's (1977) claim that there are three big ethical questions to address. They may go a long way toward comprehending ethical problems. But just as importantly, they help establish what moral decisions would prove best for the complex ethical decisions we often encounter. The three questions are:

- Who is actually making the ethical decision?
- What criteria should I use to make relevant ethical decisions?
- To whom or what do my moral obligations apply? (See Figure 2.2)

At the risk of sounding dramatic, savor the essence of what these questions are asking you to do. Pause for a moment and then re-read the questions. That short period of reflection will hopefully allow you to experience the wide point of view even for just a moment and will add to your ethical perspective.

OK, now let's examine these questions a bit more closely.

First, "Who is actually making the ethical decision?" To understand the question a bit better, we can state it another way: "Who is to make the ethical decision?" This sounds odd, because many of us assume that only we make such decisions. But the decision making can go a couple of ways. For instance, what if individuals do not make ethical decisions at all? What does that mean? Ethical decisions can be made either by individuals or by authoritarian sources. If made by authoritarian sources,

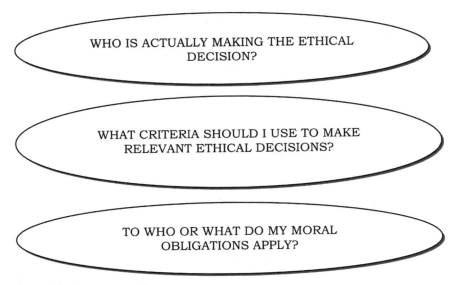

WHO IS ACTUALLY MAKING THE ETHICAL
DECISION?

WHAT CRITERIA SHOULD I USE TO MAKE
RELEVANT ETHICAL DECISIONS?

TO WHO OR WHAT DO MY MORAL
OBLIGATIONS APPLY?

Figure 2.2 Broad perspective.

then the ethical decisions are already given. Right and wrong is already established. You may see this with some of your addiction colleagues who insist on following a set course of action based on a deity, ethical standard, or whatever authority they invoke. Essentially, their stance is that you are to obey such standards or laws.

On the other hand is a standpoint called the *autonomy perspective*. It implies that we are self-determined and responsible for our own actions and decisions. We are the product of our own experience, sensibilities, and values. With this perspective, making moral decisions is not merely a matter of what one does or obeys but of what one is.

So who is making ethical decisions?

On to the second big question: "What criteria should I use to make relevant ethical decisions?" Another way to put this is to ask, "What standards or measures will I use as a basis for my ethical judgment?" The answer, unfortunately, is never easy. There are three schools of thought that attempt to answer this second question:

- The formalist
- The relativist
- The contextualist

We will run into these three in more detail a little later on, so we are going to keep the explanations brief and simple for the time being. Remember our goal here is just to try and achieve a wide ethical perspective.

The *formalist* position is one that uses a set of criteria to make relevant ethical decisions. Such criteria would include a wide-ranging (if not universal) set of laws. Examples of such criteria would include the addiction codes of ethics most counselors sign when they become certified or recertified. Knowing these codes ahead of time, you as an addiction counselor are informed of what and what not to do in terms of ethical conduct.

The next position is the *relativist* stance. While we will shortly examine this more closely, in summary the relativist position states that what is right for one person may be wrong for another. This presents significant problems for addiction ethics and for ethics in general. Stay tuned for that.

The third is the *contextualist* position. Here your appropriate ethical decisions are based not on the formalist or relativist views, but rather on context. Each addiction ethics situation or dilemma is unique. Only after one collects all the relevant information and factors for a unique ethical situation can one make an informed ethical decision.

Now, the last of the big three questions posed by Christian is to whom or what do my moral obligations apply? Or, to put it another way: Who and what should I care about? Imagine a big circle around you and how far out it might extend in terms of your ethical concerns. For our purposes, would it only include you, your clients, and your circle of addiction colleagues? Might it be a bit wider and include other clients and addiction colleagues? Might it be wider yet and include clients and colleagues in other countries? Should you only care about family and friends? Should you care about people in the same country or the church denomination you belong to? Should you care about all humans? What about animals? You get the picture.

Now with this wide perspective of ethics in mind, did you happen to find yourself gravitating toward any one view? If so, you are beginning to discover something about your ethical self. That discovery may be telling you what type of penchant you have for making your ethical judgments. You are becoming more morally aware (Roberson & Garratt, 1999).

There is one last large perspective to look at, and then we can start filling in the details.

THE FULL-SCALE VIEW: ETHICAL PARAMETERS

The following parameters stake out more of the landscape ahead.

First, ethics is not ethics unless other people are involved. Ethics is all about how people exist next to one another and live with one another (Cohen, 2002) (some would include animals). If you have a persistent and unhealthy desire to sleep with one of your clients, for example, that constitutes what is called a *solitary transgression.* It is in the realm of morality. To become unethical, you have to begin the process of manipulating the desired client into going to bed with you. That action falls into the realm of ethics because someone else is involved. If you were the last person on the planet, it would be difficult to have a full set of ethical practices.

Second, with ethics *intent* counts (Cohen, 2002). Consider intent as something akin to planning and motive. It makes a profound difference in the criminal justice system if a crime is unintentional or has intent. In addiction-oriented ethics (and ethics in general), we judge unethical behavior more harshly if such behavior had a plan behind it. This is especially true if there was a clear plan to do harm. Regard the intent element in ethics as one of degree. While we may judge behaviors or actions as right or wrong (two directions), intent can be thought of as a third direction. This additional direction adds an element of refinement to ethical arguments.

But this is where advanced ethics gets a bit sticky. Why? Because not everyone agrees with intent as a criteria. There are some who dismiss intent. They are more concerned with the thing done. To them, motive counts for nothing (Samuel Butler as cited in Cohen, 2002). For example, it doesn't matter to the police if you agree with the speed laws as long as you obey them (the thing done). For those that hold to this view, it doesn't matter if a client internalizes the "no drugs allowed in the treatment program" rule, as long as that client abides by the rule. To those who dismiss intent, it is not important whether or not the client has an internal desire to obey rules. The more important thing is not to bring drugs into a treatment program. That action (thing done) would raise the possibly of being caught and therefore discharged. With this view, the client does not wish to be caught and discharged, so he does not bring drugs into a treatment program. Those who hold to this point of view would argue that regardless of the intent or motivation, the client is sober and that's enough. This is a bit of the idea behind the "fake it till you make it" slogan.

On the other hand, some might argue that you and I should be well intentioned, because it is the more noble of the two positions. But, as we all know, many well-intentioned thoughts never come to action. Many of our clients have good intentions not to use drugs but end up using them anyway. And some people can do the right thing for the wrong reason. For example, imagine a client who doesn't bring drugs into a program because he fears losing his high-paying job and prestige, yet all the while he deeply wants to use another line of cocaine. This client is doing the right thing for what some would say is the wrong reason, but he is still doing the right thing.

Yet we don't want our clients or ourselves to be dishonorable. We seemingly need to combine these different points of view because we strive to place our intentions into ethical and able actions. No matter what your view, we have to consider the effect our actions will have on others (Cohen, 2002). So let's leave this little dispute for a moment and claim that intent does have a say in morality, although it is still up for some considerable debate.

The third point—and it is a big one—is that ethics aims to resolve dilemmas (Ingram & Parks, 2002). Dilemmas are situations that place you in the position of "damned if you do, and damned if you don't" (Baggini & Fosl, 2003). Most addiction professionals will face ethical dilemmas and will need a method to resolve them. The essence of ethics is seeking what is right and wrong.

Fourth, thinking is necessary for ethics and morality (Brown, 2001; Curtler, 2004; Thomson, 1999). Ethics is a thinking process, a thinking discipline if you will. Overall, thinking advances ethics in general and ethical decision making specifically. While one may argue that ethics is a matter of personal feeling or mere opinion, such positions rarely advance ethics as well as does clear thinking. Opinion or personal feeling simply cannot offer a standard of measure beyond "my feeling or opinion is better than yours." Arguments based on feelings and personal opinion rarely advance anything but one's own feelings and personal opinions. In ethics, one has to supply a rational defensibility of one's feelings and opinions (Woodhouse, 1994). Learning how to create a rational defense is much of what constitutes critical thinking as applied in this context.

Fifth, ethics asks you to be impartial (Rachels, 1986). For you and I to conduct ethics without impartiality would present grave consequences. It would not allow societies to develop a framework of morality. Without ethical impartiality, the entirety of ethics just could not happen.

If you disagree, you need to construct an argument for how a society could build an ethical framework merely on personal belief and personal opinion. The cornerstone of such an argument would be how a society could build its framework on partiality. Keep in mind if you argue for partiality, you in turn argue for inconsistency. Ethics cannot be established with inconsistency.

Sixth, for ethics to matter, the happiness and suffering of others must matter to us. Such a perspective will connect us more deeply to others (Harris, 2005). We will address this more in chapter 3.

Seventh, formal definitions of ethics are typically stated in terms such as, *It is the study of norms and principles of conduct* (Steward & Blocker, 1982), or *a topic of right or wrong action* (Honderich, 1995). Assessing conduct or assessing what is right or wrong has at its core a judgment process no matter how you cut it. Like it or not, ethics judges human behavior (or conduct) (Woodhouse, 1994). The judgment process centers on determining what is right and wrong, and what is justice (Ingram & Parks, 2002). Moreover, one element of ethics includes telling others what is right and wrong and what is just.

Now for ethical judgments to be convincing, they need good arguments. Good arguments, as we will see, need good reasons, and good arguments and reasons need good thought. Moral philosophy is best understood as an attempt to think critically about what is right and wrong (Law, 2007). This process is especially true when it comes to telling others what is right or wrong. And make no mistake about it, we do tell others what is right and wrong, be it our children, clients, or associates.

Yet what set of standards does one use to judge right and wrong? With that little question in mind, you need to know that whatever standard you choose, it is not going to be perfect for all ethical dilemmas. No theory of ethics is going to be perfect, because today's addiction ethics is extraordinarily complex and constantly evolves. So attempting to select an ethical standard, and knowing (a) ethics is complex and (b) ethical standards evolve, if they do nothing else, will force you to think.

TAKING A STAND

Despite the fact that there is no perfect set of ethical standards for all situations, we again need to press that you not waffle out of making ethical decisions. We said it at the beginning of this chapter and will say it again: Despite the imperfections of today's ethics, you still need to judge the actions of others. That's right—*judge,* and *take a stand.* But when you do, such judgments should be based on solid arguments, or what others might call a solid foundation (Curtler, 2004; Thomson, 1999).

Why this insistence on judging? One response is that we do it all the time. Whether you wish to admit it or not, you judge others. You do it each and every time you hear clients disclose their life histories. You react on a gut level. When you read an article or hear a story about a criminal act, you react on a gut level. Some rational piece of your brain might kick in and discount that initial, primitive judgment, but you still judge. While we all do this sort of thing, it is not a sufficient reason to continue doing it.

A second, perhaps more important reason for insisting on judging rests on not making a judgment when in fact you should. Waffling or trying to not judge may be seen as somehow fair and nonoffensive. Yet, as with anything, such a position can be dangerous if taken too far. We are a species that makes mistakes, and often they are of a moral or ethical nature. A position of nonjudgment when judgment is required is wrong. Consider not chastising children when they hit a fellow sibling, or not chastising if a child steals and claims another's toy as his own. To idly sit by and not judge would not be productive to any civilization. Children have to be taught right and wrong. Judging such actions are the first steps in that process. In these and many other situations, avoiding judgment would be wrong.

Should you disagree with this argument, create an argument to support not judging each time one child hits another. More to the point, make an argument of maintaining moral neutrality when someone is raped or murdered or offended in some other way. Pushed to the limit, what would a society look like without judgment?

Finally, judging others isn't all that bad. Some circles would have you believe otherwise. Some would insist you not judge acts such as flying airplanes into skyscrapers, or burning heretics at the stake, because of various religious, cultural, or political reasons. The problem with those positions is that they shut down dialogue. They place themselves above ethics and state that certain peoples or behaviors are off limits to any judgments. Such statements are dogmatic and close-minded. This is hardly an atmosphere of healthy discourse.

In summary, you are again encouraged to judge, but to do it with thought and reason.

All this takes us to the next step—a brief introduction to critical thinking.

CRITICAL THINKING BASICS

Much of this book deals with how to apply critical thinking principles to moral reasoning. In order to proceed, we need to briefly outline some basic elements of critical thinking.

At this juncture, we need to remind you that this is not so much a book on what you *should* do as it is one on how you can conduct, perform, or accomplish your own moral reasoning. Being able to do this is where critical thinking comes in. It gives you suggestions on *how* to think, not *what* to think.

First things first, take a position about addiction ethics—or, better yet, make a judgment call about an addiction ethics situation and already you have made an argument. All arguments consist of reasons that support a conclusion (see Figure 2.3). For example, one such argument might be: "I think it's wrong to tell clients who have been prescribed medications by a medical doctor to stop taking them. This is contrary to the position of some who believe all medications are considered drugs, which have the potential to interfere with a recovery process. There is no data to substantiate that claim, and some recovering folks need medication.

Figure 2.3 Basic argument.

In addition, it's wrong because no matter what you think of doctors or how strongly you feel the importance of being completely drug free is to recovery, you are not a doctor, and you have no right to give advice in something you know little about." This little argument contains a set of reasons (there is no data, you are not a doctor, you have no right to give advice) that support a conclusion (lay people should not tell others to get off medications).

With that established, we now need to distinguish between everyday clinical conclusions, administrative decisions, or supervisory arguments, versus actual moral arguments.

Distinguishing between ordinary arguments and moral arguments is not that simple. Both are trying to win you over to a particular position. Moral arguments usually recommend a position based on a value—such as whether behavior is good or bad, or whether a particular choice is a good one or bad one. Clinical decisions are more about what is the best diagnosis and thus the best treatment for a client. (Note that even these questions have an element of right and wrong associated with them.)

Moral arguments often use words like "should" and "ought." For example: "The ethical addiction counselor *should not* take personal advantage of clients" or "Ethical counselors *ought* to strive for honesty in their daily work, because they cannot be ethical otherwise." However, words like "should" and "ought" can equally apply to clinical arguments such as, "I believe cognitive-behavioral strategies *should* be applied to this particular client."

Moral arguments often use words such as "right" and "wrong." For example: "By reporting the unethical behavior of a fellow counselor, Bob did the *right* thing" or "It is unmistakably *wrong* to extract more insurance funds from a client simply because the client has such insurance." In addition, moral arguments often use certain adjectives such as *cruel, dishonest,* and *improper* (Thomson, 1999). Here is an illustration: "To verbally attack clients is cruel." The use of these terms is generally, but not always, a tip that one is making a moral argument.

Yet while regular arguments and moral arguments might look the same, sometimes the form or shape of the argument will differentiate them. For example, regular arguments usually include an action for you to follow and an entreaty that it would be prudent to do so, such as, "To improve your chances of avoiding lung cancer, you should refrain from smoking cigarettes." Prudent advice. On the other hand, a moral argument may not have a particular aim (avoiding lung cancer); however, it does have an entreaty to do something simply because it is the right (or wrong) thing to do, such as, "To maintain a positive role model as an addiction counselor, it is recommended you avoid using illegal drugs. It is just the right thing to do." There are some other conditions that describe the components of a moral argument, but these guidelines are a good start (Thomson, 1999).

ETHICAL SELF-EXAM

A good way to end this chapter is with a quick self-exam. When discussing ethics one cannot help but begin to think about the question: How do you ethically conduct your personal and professional life? To get to some kind of an answer, we often resort to other questions, such as the following:

- Do you live via or through a certain set of ethical (moral) standards?
- If you do, could you easily spell them out if asked, or would you find yourself having trouble coming to an answer?
- If you do have standards, essentially what are they? (Write out a list.)
- Do you assess different ethical situations by the same standards or do you use different standards for different ethical situations?
- If you do assess different situations by different standards, what reasons can you cite for this action?
- Do you ever cheat on your standards? If so, on what particular circumstances do you usually or most often cheat?
- Do you judge others with one set of standards and judge your actions by a different set?
- If so, can you recall the last time you did this, and on what did you cheat?

These questions are intended to bring up a few points. The first is to determine if indeed you have a set of ethical standards with which you judge yourself and others. Second, if pressed, could you defend the credibility of your ethics? That is, could you make rational ethical statements and provide good solid reasons in your defense? If you cannot provide viable responses for your standards, then read on and see if you can connect with some of the grand ethical stances that are coming up.

For now, if you are finding it difficult to list your ethical standards or are discovering that they are not very clear, here are a few quick clarifying points. They are often the foundation of many ethical standards.

- Ethics is about choices.
- Values cannot help but be a part of those choices. (Consider values to be principles, standards, or qualities considered worthwhile or desirable by most individuals and societies.)
- Reasons—good rational ones—should guide your choices.
- An important element in advanced ethics is determining how you came to your ethical decision, not having someone else make one for you.
- So how do you do it? (Read on.)

THE LEAST YOU NEED TO KNOW

- Ethical decisions will require you to take a stand.
- Ethics talks the talk, and morality walks the walk.
- The three *big* questions are:
  - Who is actually making the ethical decision?
  - What criteria should I use to make relevant ethical decisions?
  - To whom or what do my moral obligations apply?
- The seven parameters of addiction ethics are:
  - Ethics is not ethics unless other people are involved (perhaps animals as well).
  - With ethics, intent counts.
  - Ethics aims to resolve dilemmas.
  - Thinking is required for ethics and morality.
  - Ethics calls for you to be impartial.
  - The happiness and suffering of others must matter to us for ethics to matter.
  - Like it or not, ethics judges human behavior.
- Conclusions should be based on reasons.

3

The Emotional Aspect
of Ethical Thinking

Much of this chapter addresses the emotional side of ethical thinking. To set the stage for that discussion, we start with what we know about biology and moral thinking and connect that to the role emotions intuitively play in our decision making. Then we look at the need for emotions in addiction ethics judgments. This chapter also continues the policy of encouraging you to perform a self-examination. Let's find out to what ideas you might connect and relate.

YOUR BRAIN AND MORAL JUDGMENTS

With all the talk in previous chapters about judgment and taking a stand, this might be a good spot to quickly summarize which parts of your brain actually judge moral issues. Yes, science has been able to locate the parts of your brain that are involved in making judgments. By virtue of brain imaging, a team of researchers at Dartmouth College (as cited in Gazzaniga, 2008) found that when you and I encounter difficult moral scenarios, the *posterior superior temporal sulcus* (STS) lights up. This area is around the level of your ears. When you are faced with a less difficult or more routine scenario, your *anterior* STS lights up. (The STS is not the only area to light up when you are faced with such dilemmas, but it is an important region.)

But things are not that simple. The brain often spreads its moral work around. So when you ponder moral issues, parts of your *frontal lobe* light up, as does a region called the *anterior cingulated cortex,* located in the back of your brain. That's the part of the brain that recognizes conflict.

Now that you know where all the moral work takes place in your brain, let's dig a little further into biology and moral thinking.

BIOLOGY AND MORAL DECISION MAKING

When it comes to making moral choices, there is evidence that we don't do it very well (Marcus, 2008). For one thing, we seem to make different moral decisions based on our visceral feelings. For example, if you see a runaway trolley about to hit five people, and you alone are in a position to throw a switch that will divert the trolley onto another track that will kill only one person, what would you do?

Now compare that situation to this one: To save the five people from the runaway trolley, you must push a single large person onto the track. The person would surely die but by weight alone would divert the trolley. What would you do? Most folks would have an easier time throwing the switch than pushing someone to his or her death. There is something visceral about the latter scenario that we generally don't like.

The point of this little exercise is that while we would like to believe we bring deliberate moral reasoning to our decisions, our emotions play a big part. There are certain acts that simply feel wrong, and scientists are at a bit of a loss to explain why. You might call these quick reactions *moral intuitions.* The very thought of parents having sex with their children, for example, makes one feel icky. You just know it's wrong! Marcus (2008) suggests that this is an illustration of when the emotional and judicial sides of the brain conflict and the emotional side wins. This instinctive wrong feeling may stem from the older parts of our brain and may override whatever the rational parts have to say about it.

Neuroimaging studies can help us understand the fast, gut reaction we often have when faced with certain moral situations. Recall the runaway trolley scenarios previously mentioned. Experimental trials have shown that those who would save the five lives at the expense of one relied on their *prefrontal cortex* (which is partial to reasoning) to make that decision. Those who decided not to sacrifice the one for the many relied more on their *limbic cortex,* which is the home of our emotions (Marcus, 2008).

So, based on this information, what will be your first impulse when faced with moral and ethical addiction decisions? It generally will be an emotional one. If we are stuck with our emotions, some argue, why not utilize them to be fair-minded when it comes to making ethical decisions?

FAIR-MINDEDNESS AND EMOTION

As we have seen, ethical dilemmas usually produce an emotional impact—sometimes a quite strong one. Such feelings are often a sign of moral seriousness (Rachels, 1986). Strong emotions are not to be confused with moderate and useful emotions, as we shall see later. However, strong emotions usually include components of favoritism and, dare we say, narrow mindedness. These strong elements cannot carry us far in addiction ethics judgments.

Are we therefore to dispose of our emotions when it comes to making ethical judgments? Not quite. As Thomson (1999) argues, we should not morally judge merely on our own unexamined feelings. At the same time, we also need to evaluate how our emotions might conflict or interfere with important moral values we face in the addiction field. This takes us then to the question: On what do we emotionally rely and use to assist with our decision making?

Some might argue for the concept of *fair-mindedness.* Roughly speaking, fair-mindedness is being honest, fair, and making judgments free from discrimination or duplicity. Moreover, fair-mindedness means being sympathetic with other views, but also with intellectual honesty, and without reference to one's vested interest or advantage (Paul, 1993; Thomson, 1999).

Fair-mindedness entails tolerance for other points of view. This can come about by listening politely, giving certain weight to an opposing view, but not by granting equal weight to all views. Granting equal weight would be a prescription for never coming to a moral conclusion (Thomson, 1999).

Say we find ourselves in a situation where we face an ethical decision on a client's active drinking behavior. The client is verbally abusive when drinking, which is harming her family, and for this reason, some argue, she should be discharged from our program. We are confronted by an opposing view to which we should give equal weight: the client is a nice person when not drinking and therefore should be kept in treatment. If we give equal weight to both views, we run the risk of never arriving at a decision. So we can give equal weight to opposing ethical viewpoints up to a certain point. That point might be how reasonable the opposing view is. Certainly, a moral view based merely on capricious thought and frivolous emotion would not be considered reasonable.

On the other hand, fair-mindedness does entail exposing your ethics to the same standards to which you subject other positions. It means making ethical decisions devoid of your special interests and advantage (Paul, 1993; Thomson, 1999). It also means judging yourself and others in the light of a few core values. Depending on who you talk to or read, there are three such critical values—avoid harm, respect autonomy, and respect justice (much more on this later). Hold these values and you cannot easily escape the emotions that accompany them, for example sympathy. Without this particular feeling, it would indeed be difficult to care for others (Thomson, 1999).

But as an aside, there are different ways you can act sympathetically, and this speaks volumes for the elements of favoritism and fair-mindedness. As an illustration, say an addiction counselor holds a favored, sympathetic, perception of a client, who unfortunately keeps on breaking small rules of the inpatient treatment program. The client and the counselor have developed a strong bond, and the counselor, in turn, is apt to (sympathetically) look the other way when the rules are broken, in the hopes that giving more chances to this person will prove in the end beneficial to the overall treatment. However, the other counselors point out that this approach is not fair-minded but is instead favoritism, which may be sending a wrong message to the client. In this situation, the bottom line is to assess to what extent your (sympathetic) feelings should be taken into a fair-minded account.

That takes us to using your emotions wisely, and brings us to the next section.

THE PLACE OF EMOTION IN ETHICAL DECISION MAKING

Before we start this section, bear in mind that part of your overall charge while reading this text is one of ongoing self-examination. Therefore you are encouraged to self-assess your position regarding the variety of moral dilemmas that follow. In particular, assess how your personal feelings come into play when you make ethical judgments, and how they affect your fair-mindedness.

Thomson (1999) would argue that our emotions have a proper role to play in ethical decision making. Far from being irrational disturbances to our rational thinking, emotions are a way of accurately reading the world. For example, anger can be an accurate perception of being treated badly. Some emotions have a clear connection with morality (more on this later).

To be fair-minded in our ethical decision making, we must assess how our emotions come into play on such decisions and help us understand the feelings and emotions of others. Thomson (1999) would go further and state that we cannot become emotionless in order to make good ethical judgments. Excluding our unexamined feelings would not increase our fair-mindedness. We need to evaluate whether our emotional responses are appropriate for a situation or if they conflict with certain moral values (Thomson, 1999). For example, ignoring a client's heightened level of loneliness and emotional pain caused by being in your treatment program and away from home for the first time simply because you have a personal dislike for that client is hardly fair-minded.

Pizarro (2000) also examines the role of emotions in ethical decision making. He makes a number of important arguments for keeping (yes, keeping) feelings in the ethical judgment process.

First, he argues that far from being antagonistic to moral decision-making, emotions play a vital role in moral judgments and should not be dismissed as inappropriate or harmful to the process, as has traditionally been the case. Pizarro acknowledges that emotions do play favorites, especially around people we care about. A classic case is the concerned mother pleading to a judge that her son is a good boy, despite the fact that he is facing his third DUI and a charge of involuntary manslaughter. Playing favorites flies in the face of the idea that we should try to be impartial in our moral evaluations. (Just try and suggest impartiality to the concerned mother.) Yet, without question, you and I generally feel more emotional about those closer to us.

Moreover, we are more emotionally aroused about issues that are closer to us. Just observe individuals in our field who bristle at the thought of addiction being considered a sin. For them, such a thought is indeed immoral. Yet when emotions are involved within the ethical decision-making process, one becomes more aware of other variables of an ethical dilemma (what is called *moral contingency* or unforeseen events or circumstances). This heightened awareness may lead to examining possible moral variables that a more rational approach would not consider. This extra perception may then lead to better decisions. To put it simply, without the emotional element, one could easily overlook important variables that need to be contained in an ethical decision.

Second, emotions are said to be arbitrary, meaning that they can be chancy and capricious. For instance, say you are a program supervisor, and you are either in a particularly happy or depressed mood when you face a serious ethical decision about a colleague's behavior. Consider what impact either mood might have on your decision.

It is often believed that emotions are devoid of rational influence and simply happen to us without voluntary control. Despite these beliefs, Pizarro argues that we should not think that emotions can never aid and will always harm moral judgments, as in the supervisor needing to make a moral decision while under the influence of strong emotion. He cites a few reasons. For one, humans have the capacity to regulate their emotions. We often induce or suppress emotions using various strategies. For example, you can break out a favorite tune on your iPod and elicit a mood, or simply recall certain memories to evoke a smile or frown on your face. This means that the supervisor certainly has the capacity to take a few minutes to compose him or herself before making the decision, thus settling the effects of the overly happy or sad mood.

Third, emotions are not solely reflexive or without rational influence. Emotions often mirror, in an affective way, our preexisting moral beliefs and principles. They easily pick up on moral and ethical infractions specific to, for example, feelings associated with victimization of an addiction client, or feelings of disgust that might come from a blatant boundary violation by a colleague. Certainly, strong moral situations do not occur without affecting one's moral belief system. But, as with the responsible addiction supervisor mentioned previously, people can and do adjust their feelings when they have to blend their reason and emotion for important ethical decisions.

Fourth, rather than diminish the reasoning process, emotions can help our reasoning by acting as a focusing agent that makes us alert to features of an ethical circumstance that might have otherwise escaped our attention. Often, they give substance to our partially formed moral judgments, by adding depth and perhaps motivation to do something about an addiction ethics situation. Moreover, controlled emotions can focus our attention and concentration on a problem. Under these circumstances, reason cannot but be enhanced by such restrained emotions. Plus, it is argued that emotions add power and energy to our desire to do good and avoid the bad.

We need to add one last point on this issue of emotions and the decision-making process. According to Gazzaniga (2008), brain research is finding that before we make a decision, an emotional response is evoked. Simply put, our emotions are always associated with moral and ethical situations. According to the research Gazzaniga has uncovered, no matter how many rational ideas a person comes up with when making a decision, emotion, at some level, is always also involved. Emotions play an important role in our decision making. They tell you that you have a conscience and scruples.

THE MORAL EMOTIONS

All this talk of emotion takes us to the point that, as humans, we generally don't make our initial ethical judgments with a great deal of reason. We judge emotionally first and then rationalize later (Shermer, 2004). Moreover, we tend to use certain emotions to make up our moral sense (Gazzaniga, 2005). The intensity of any one or combination of these emotions will sway the way we think. And if that isn't enough, we generally use the first argument that satisfies our belief or opinion, and then cease thinking (Gazzaniga, 2008). It is a "makes sense to me" feeling that prompts the negation of additional thought.

Since we generally judge emotionally first and think later, it might be a good time to examine this process more closely. Not all the emotions humans possess apply to morality. There has been considerable thought over what are called *moral emotions*. At the risk of simplifying this deliberation, and focusing mainly on Western thought, I will say that moral emotions can be a quick and sometimes reliable response to social events and moral standards (Tangney, Stuewig, & Mashek, 2007). They are difficult to counterfeit, and, if awakened, they signal the existence of a conscience (Gazzaniga, 2008).

Here we will examine the four broad family groups of moral emotions. They are divided into two large and two small families. Each family contains a set of subtype emotions (Haidt, 2003). The large families consist of the following:

- The *other condemning* emotions. These are emotions with an element of disapproval often directed outward toward the likes of liars, cheaters, and those who do negative things to others. There are three subtypes.

- *Anger*—Anger is sometimes considered the underappreciated moral emotion, usually thought of as an immoral emotion, and often associated with violence. However, anger can be seen as a sense of indignity, standing up for what is right, and demanding justice. This indignity is sometimes seen in addiction stigma, which can pigeonhole clients with an addiction and does not give them a second chance in life. A second type of anger is the *righteous* type. Here the anger is elicited by the violation of a moral standard, where the harm was not personally experienced but was seen as repulsive behavior aimed at another, and it can thereby motivate third parties to take action (Tangney et al., 2007). This can be seen as the motivating factor used by individuals who witness DUI drivers harm others with little or no consequences. These righteous angry individuals then form national organizations to reduce or stop such behavior.
- *Disgust*—This is a revolted response to physical objects (such as excrement) and social violations, such as hypocrisy, betrayal, or cruelty. It can be the first emotion felt toward people who degrade themselves, as is sometimes seen with those with substance abuse who, in the height of their addiction, do unpleasant things to obtain money for their next drug. It may also be a person's first emotional response to a drug-related news story.
- *Contempt*—This often falls between anger and disgust, where one feels morally superior by looking down on others, as in so-called normal folks looking down at the homeless.

- The *self-conscious emotions* are emotions that tend to monitor and constrain one's own behavior. There are three subtypes.

  - *Guilt*—This is often elicited by violation of moral rules, particularly so if such violations cause harm or suffering to others. Guilt judges your bad actions. Guilt often motivates people to confess so as to restore loving relationships. This is sometimes seen with recovering individuals who make amends to those they harmed during their active addiction days.
  - *Shame*—This emotion runs deeper than guilt. It runs to the very core of one's self. As with guilt, it is elicited by bad actions, but shame is the result of violating a social norm while someone is watching. It triggers one to hide and withdraw (Gazzaniga, 2008). It is a failure to measure up to a significant moral and/or

cultural standard. Shame is darker and more painful than guilt. Where guilt motivates people to redeem themselves, shame provokes denial, a propensity to hide or escape, and a propensity to externalize blame or experience intense anger in destructive ways coupled with aggression (Tangney et al., 2007). This aggression can be seen sometimes in a shamed partner retaliating against a significant other.

- *Embarrassment*—This is less relevant to morality than guilt or shame but is associated with the humiliation and mortification that is often felt when one violates a social convention or when one does not behave properly or loses face, generally around people of higher status. This can be seen with certain intoxicated behavior in public.

The small moral emotional families consist of the following:

- The *other praising emotions* are outwardly directed emotions and represent the bright side of emotions, because they are sensitive to good deeds and exemplary models. They may motivate individuals to engage in helping behavior (Gazzaniga, 2008). They have two subtypes.

  - *Gratitude*—This is defined as being appreciative, warm, and friendly toward a benefactor or program that is perceived to have done an good deed for you. Generally, the receivers of a good deed feel indebtedness, and that feeling tends to make individuals act more prosocially—as individuals in Alcoholics Anonymous and similar self-help groups feel indebted to those programs.

  - *Elevation*—This emotion is elicited by acts of kindness, self-sacrifice, and charity that open one's heart to the ones who triggered the elevation and prompt us to perform similar acts. This is often seen around the holiday season.

- The *other suffering emotions* are emotions that rouse feelings in ourselves and motivate us to action. There are three subtypes.

  - *Sympathy*—This is said to the basis of morality. We as a species generally feel bad when we see others suffer, and we are inclined to offer help. Addiction counselors often experience this when clients convey their active addiction history with a tone of remorse and regret. We often then feel the strong urge to help such a client as much as we can.

- *Compassion*—This is being moved by another's misery and suffering; however, there is a twinge of guilt associated with compassion, and it is often more acutely felt by those closer to us. As with sympathy, it stirs us to help, rather than just feeling bad for the others. Compassion provides the force to actually do something. Again, it can be seen in the eyes of many addiction counselors.
- *Empathy*—While this is technically not an emotion, it is the ability to feel whatever another person (such as a client) is feeling. That includes the gamut of feelings from anger to worthlessness. The ability to feel what others feel often, in turn, elicits the sympathy and compassion seen in a vast number of addiction counselors.

We need to insert a final note about emotions. It has to do with how increasing emotions can affect moral judgments. Some research indicates that those subjects who had had their emotional levels increased tended to interpret neutral stories with a moral edge (Tangney et al., 2007). The point of this is to advise readers that their heightened emotions may indeed bias their moral judgments.

MORAL PRIDE

As noted, not all moral emotions are associated with negative emotions; they do have a positive side. We could not leave this section without a quick look at *moral pride* (Tangney et al., 2007). It is a feeling that elicits a certain level of self-respect—as in the act of returning a lost wallet intact to a complete stranger or associate. This type of behavior enhances self-worth and often encourages one to strive to maintain such standards. One can see this in addiction counselors who have maintained a certain level of dignity over their careers. They have treated clients and colleagues with respect, have not maligned others, have not allowed themselves to engage in fraudulent behavior, have not overly trumpeted themselves at the expense of others, and have not used morality as a shield to belittle others. Generally, they are very nice people to be around.

This discussion of moral emotions and moral pride is meant to serve as a barometer for you to self-assess and become more familiar with how you judge ethical situations. Some would have you believe that emotions cloud judgment; however, going to the other end of the spectrum and claiming that one has to be emotionless in order to be fair-minded is not a good idea. Humans are just not constructed to make decisions without some element of personal feelings. The point, as Thomson (1999) has aptly stated, is that we should not make moral judgments based solely on unchecked and raw feelings. As addiction professionals, we need to consider whether our emotional response to an ethical situation is appropriate and whether our emotions conflict with other moral values. For example, are we overreacting to an addiction-related incident, or are we offering too much sympathy for a favored client?

THE LEAST YOU NEED TO KNOW

- Different parts of your brain light up when faced with moral situations.
- Humans don't make moral choices very well.
- Fair-mindedness is being honest, fair, and free from bigotry and deception when making ethical judgments.
- Emotions have a fitting role to play in ethical decision making. Far from being irrational disturbances to rational thinking, emotions are a way of accurately reading the world.
- Moral emotions can be a reliable response to social events and moral standards, and they come in several forms:
  - Other condemning emotions
  - Self-conscious emotions
  - Other praising emotions
  - Other suffering emotions
- Moral pride elicits a level of self-respect and enhances self-worth.

4   A Few Moral Issues to Generate Thought and Feeling

Over the past several chapters you covered a number of basic moral concepts, and you hung in there. Good for you! It is time to put some of this into practice. The point of this short chapter is to get you thinking and utilizing the material that has been presented. Plus, it is designed to produce feelings so you become aware of the moral emotions you use when you judge.

This chapter introduces various ethical issues and dilemmas. Not all of them have to do with addiction ethics. Some folks may wonder why I bring up non–addiction ethics issues. The answer is that we will use these examples as a warm-up. If you can formulate good judgments about some of these examples, you will have gained practice for the big addiction ethics issues that follow later in the book.

This chapter is designed to review your present level of judgment. You may find that some of these scenarios get your blood boiling, which is the point—so you see how well you think and feel under the heat. It's exactly the kind of warm-up to do before getting to the next chapter on formal ethical positions.

The examples start easy and gradually become more complex. They are not presented with answers. The goals are to (a) make you think, (b) apply what you presently have in your inventory of moral decision-making skills, and (c) employ what has been presented in the previous chapters. In other words, this is just a modest mental workout.

This chapter is purposely brief. We don't want to overload you with a lot of examples; more will come later in the book.

MORAL ISSUES

We will start with a list of nonaddiction scenarios just to get you thinking. We have Steven Pinker (2002) to thank for this list (abbreviated for our use) of moral issues. While he discusses why the items on this list have acquired a moral dimension, I want you to assess why you think each item should (or should not) be considered a moral issue. Whether you are in favor or opposed to the stated item, try to create an argument for a stand.

Take, for example, fast food. Does fast food have a moral component? Those who argue that fast food *is* a moral issue might state the following:

- Eating fast food makes people overweight.
- The cheap price of fast food makes it attractive to people who cannot afford other options.
- The poor nutritional quality of most fast food leads to health problems.
- The lack of labeling to indicate nutritional value of fast food leads to deceptive practices.
- The methods of production to supply fast food are inherently cruel (environmental consequences, inhuman treatment of animals).
- The emotional angle. It just upsets me to see how many people use this fattening product over and over again. I just think it's wrong.

On the other hand, those who argue that fast food is *not* a moral issue might state the following:

- People can always choose not to partake of fast food; they eat it of their own free will, and thus it is not a moral issue (which negates all the other moral premises).
- Moral arguments against this product make it sound as if people who eat fast food products are merely pawns at the mercy of big corporations; they are not.

- Most fast food restaurants now clearly list calories and nutritional information, so customers know what they are ingesting.
- While food inspections are a good practice, it is unfair to hold fast food to a higher standard than other industries are subject to.
- "I should be allowed to eat what I want; no one should be able to tell me what to eat" (the emotional argument).

While your analysis does not need to be as in-depth as this, the idea is still to create arguments for and against the items on the list.

- Executive salaries
- Automobile safety
- Barbie dolls
- Clothing that is manufactured in the third world
- Defense-funded research
- Toy guns
- Fur
- Logging
- Nuclear power
- Oil drilling
- Public holidays (e.g., Columbus Day)
- Sugar
- Spanking
- Weight of fashion models

COMMON ETHICAL DILEMMAS

Some of the situations that follow were modified from the St. James Ethics Centre Web page (*Ethical Dilemmas*, 2008). For each situation, ask yourself the following questions: What are the ethical issues involved? What should you do? What would you do?

- Should you be honest and tell your good friend something that would most certainly hurt his or her feelings, or should you spare him or her the hurt?
- Should you respect your teenager by allowing him or her to make a risky adult decision, or should you deny him or her the choice?
- Do you commit a mentally incompetent parent to a medical care facility, or do you obey his/her wish that you personally take care of him or her despite the hardship imposed on you?

■ After dinner in a nice restaurant, you notice you did not get charged for a nice dessert. Do you inform the wait staff?

MORE CHALLENGING ETHICAL DILEMMAS

It's time to kick it up a notch. What follows are ethical situations that have actually come out of the news. As with the previous examples, you are encouraged to first review the story, then make your judgments.

Traffic Death

Recently in the news, a highway video camera captured a hit-and-run accident. The video clearly shows an automobile hitting a 78-year-old man as he flips feet first over the roof of the car that struck him (Singer, 2008).

Two things were reported and were clearly observed. One, the car that hit the man plainly did not stop. Second, the paralyzed man lay on the highway for some time while people and cars passed him. Some looked and stared, but no one helped. (The police who eventually arrived were on another call and just happened to have found the stricken individual.)

The sheriff who investigated the incident stated, "The city has lost its moral compass." He further stated, "Whoever did this should be sent away for a long time. It was as if he (the victim) was a dog left in the street to die."

■ What is your first emotional reaction as you read this?
■ What would be your reaction if the driver were found to be under the influence?
■ What would be your reaction if the driver who hit this individual were found to be sober?
■ If the driver were found to be intoxicated at the time, arrested and sentenced to treatment, how would you react if the driver ended up as a client of yours?

Father With Teething Infant

Another news story. This one involves a father who was sentenced to life in prison. Apparently his infant son died after sucking on the father's cocaine-tainted finger. The father reported he fell asleep with the baby on his chest, and when he awoke the baby was not breathing. The father admitted that he was cutting up cocaine, and soon after the baby began to suck on the father's fingers. The coroner determined that the baby had undigested cocaine in its stomach and testified that the cocaine could have caused the acute toxicity. In addition, the father had a record of eight previous convictions, six of which were cocaine related.

- What is your first emotional reaction to this case?
- Do you think a life-term is the most appropriate sentence for the father, or would you press for another action? Outline your reasons.

Ice-Using Mother

Not long ago, a female in a western state gave birth to a stillborn baby. Four hours prior to the birth, she managed to get off the hospital grounds and smoke a pipe full of crack. In fact, she had been abusing crack all through her pregnancy. The coroner's report indicated that the drug use was a key factor in the death of the baby.

The mother was incarcerated for a short time and then later released. The rationale for the release came from a ruling by the state's supreme court. They ruled that since the state law indicated that an unborn child was not considered human, the defendant should be set free. And so she was.

The issue hit the newspapers and struck hard at many in the community. Many individuals felt that the legal decision did not address the deep moral and ethical issues of the case.

Some of those issues centered on the following questions.

- Did the woman do something wrong or not?
- Was she responsible for the death of a baby? If so, should she have been given more than a short prison term?
- Is a baby who is not yet born considered human or not? (This question brings us closer to the heated abortion debate, and all its ramifications.)
- And, finally, should someone under the influence of substances be held accountable for his or her actions, or should he or she be excused because he or she is considered to have a disease over which he or she has no control?

Much of the argument boiled down to the fact that some people in the community wanted the mother to pay a steeper price for the incident (more prison time). After all, they thought, she did something morally wrong. Others said that because she expressed regret and sorrow for the stillbirth, and endured so much personal pain, that she had already paid a high enough price; nothing would be gained by giving the mother more prison time. (As a follow-up, the mother did complete a drug and alcohol treatment program, and as of this writing remains substance free.)

There are surely other ethical elements involved in this case, but it sets the tone for the complicated issues addiction professionals face. The point of all this is to highlight how involved addiction ethics has become. Even if you do not know this case personally, somewhere somehow you have thoughts and feelings about it and what should have been done. But the pivotal questions are: What would be your ethical decision? What do you believe is the most ethical course of action? And, most importantly, how did you come to that decision?

THE LEAST YOU NEED TO KNOW

- What were your initial feelings when you read each story?
- How did you frame your ethical judgments?

Ethical Theories and Applications

5   An Array of Moral Foundations

This is an atypical chapter for an addiction professional audience. The intent is to introduce addiction professionals to philosophical ideas and philosophers that can play significant roles in addiction ethics decisions. And play a role they do, whether you realize it or not. The point is to put a name to the moral ideas you have tucked away in the back of your mind. Naming and discussing various moral positions will provide clarity and direction for future ethical encounters.

Frankly, one does not see such ideas mentioned for study or consideration in the addiction field. It is time to change that. In this day and age, addiction professionals need all the help we can get to address our thorny ethical problems.

YOUR INTUITIVE ETHICAL TENDENCIES

Over the ages, a number of moral and ethical views have been created. What's more, each of these positions had a number of spin-offs, and then more spin-offs were generated from those. Trying to understand all that will make your head spin (sorry). While becoming familiar with some of those views is one goal of this chapter, an ancillary goal is to allow you to find the viewpoint to which you naturally gravitate.

We all have our own intuitive ethical tendencies. Putting a name to that intuitive perspective not only clearly identifies a favored ethical view but helps clarify the general methods you use to judge ethical situations. And for what it's worth, while you may find a core ethical standard to your liking, you will also uncover your biases. However, once this is established, you are in a better position to defend why, when faced with an ethical situation, you made a particular judgment. Moreover, you can confidently defend your judgment against any and all who wish to confront you. Finally, making thoughtful ethical judgments helps you to sleep a little better at night.

So here's the tough part. You are to push yourself in this chapter to establish (or re-establish) your favored ethical standards. You are not allowed to maintain a wishy-washy "I don't know what my moral ethical standards are" position. No, no, no! This is partly a thinking book, partly a critical thinking book. As such, it requires that you really explore your thoughts. Doing that requires not only asking tough questions of others but also asking tough questions of yourself.

Here's the easy part. The chapter makes a strong effort to keep all the complicated nomenclature and philosophical ramblings to a minimum. It will just briefly cover the principal views. Thus, what follows are simplified versions of various (and in some cases complicated) philosophical positions. This book is not about debating esoteric philosophical discussions. For those so inclined, please see the references for more information.

To repeat, the most important thing to get out of this chapter is to identify with one or more of the positions. After you read a section, try to assess if the position feels natural or sits well with you. You will then have a handle on how your heart makes ethical judgments. That's important because you need to really know that position, not just feel it. Second, you can then assess and contrast the pros and cons of your favored position with the others. Third, hopefully your judgment system will evolve after you have seen some other points of view and have given them all careful thought. Since you are being asked to make (not shy away from) ethical judgments, you should have a good idea of what constitutes your decision-making foundation.

Once established, you can ask if your viewpoint is the most appropriate for the addiction ethics problems you will face or perhaps consider if other options might be more appropriate for a certain dilemma.

FORMAL ETHICAL CONCEPTS

Because philosophical concepts have been known to cause panic and fear in some folks, let's start easy. This initial look will also keep step with our ethical perspective. Then we will get a little more formal but still keep the concepts uncomplicated.

Ethical theories can be bunched into broad categories that share a common theme. Thompson (2003) has placed a number of ethical ideas into a broad concept or theme of how we know about things. (If you really want to know the term for how we know things, it's called *epistemology*). What might be helpful here is to understand this as a question. How, for example, do we really know what the word "good" means? Sounds dumb, I know, but bear with me for a minute. Of course, some folks would say, I know what "good" means. Yet the little problem is how do you know that your definition is really accurate, compared to the next guy? Philosophers love to ask these kinds of questions.

Well, it turns out there are ways to find out what "good" means. In our case, we look at four of these ways as arranged by Thompson (2003). Now, there are philosophical problems with each, but that is not our worry at this time. Let's just get the concepts.

Intuitionism

Our first view comes with the imposing-sounding name of *intuitionism*. Simply put, it says that we know and understand things because we instinctively (on a gut level) know them. In terms of the word "good," we know something as good because over the years "good" for us has become self-evident and obvious. For example, imagine seeing someone in an AA meeting reach out to a nervous new member. That's a good act. We just know it.

Emotivism

The next view is called *emotivism*. Here, morality is reduced to your emotional response to observing an act. "Good" is a matter of feeling. As illustrated by the preceding example, watching the AA member reach out to a newcomer will often make you, as an observer, feel good (not to mention the feeling the newcomer might have).

Prescriptivism

Third on our list is called *prescriptivism*. In this case, we prescribe or specify something as good. Staying with our AA example, witnessing the act of reaching out to our nervous newcomer, the person standing beside you states, "That was a good act." The person prescribed the act as good right as it happened. Simple enough.

Naturalism

Last is a view called *naturalism*. This view relates moral features to certain features of the world and certain social relationships. While rooted in science, which only describes what is not what ought to be, naturalism would still argue moral judging is a natural activity of humans. Using our AA example, several members observe the act of reaching out and all judge that the act was good and further judge that the act should be considered good. "Wasn't it good that Frank reached out to the new guy," says one guy. And all within earshot nod in agreement. Again, simple.

We now know how various views define the concept of good. Seeing different views is OK, even if it does not give us one universal view. A variety of concepts is more typical in ethics than a single, all-encompassing view. Of particular note is for you to determine which of the views most resonates with you. If you found it, you have discovered something ethically interesting about how you judge (see Figure 5.1).

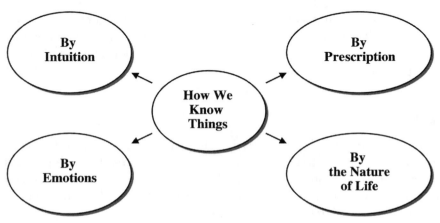

Figure 5.1 How we know things.

OK, if you got this, you can see our broad ethical landscape or perspective. Now it's time to move on to something a little more formal.

FOUR MAIN ETHICAL THEORIES

We will first cover four fundamental moral points of view (Rauhut, 2006). These are a little more formal in that they present not only a view of ethics but also an idea of how we should then act in accordance with that view. We will offer a short criticism for each, nothing extravagant, but enough for you to see that no formal ethical ideas are above criticism. Following this discussion, we then offer a few other moral views. Somewhere in all this, you should be able to find more of what guides your addiction ethics decision making. The four major views are first outlined, diagrammed (see Figure 5.2), and then detailed. The four views (outline version) are:

- Religion based—This position is rooted in *divine command;* actions are morally right if they are in agreement with God's commands. Does this sound like something from which you make your addiction-oriented ethical judgments?
- Duty based—This position is founded within *deontology,* where a moral action is considered right when the motive behind the action is deemed good. As such, it is then my duty to do good. And there are a priori (i.e., I don't need experience to know something, I just know it) universal moral obligations. Does this sound like

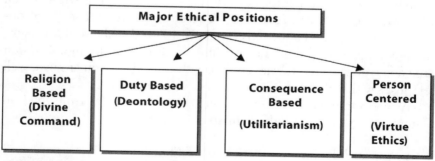

Figure 5.2 Major ethical positions.

something from which you make your addiction-oriented ethical judgments?

■ Consequence or results based—This is, essentially, the *utilitarian* position, where action is morally right if it maximizes overall well-being and happiness. Does this sound like something from which you make your addiction-oriented ethical judgments?

■ Person centered—This is the realm of *virtue ethics*, where an action is morally right if a person (agent) who has all the proper virtues would have performed the action. Does this sound like something from which you make your addiction-oriented ethical judgments?

DIVINE COMMAND

Arguably, this is what most people around the world encounter as their first understanding of morality—a religion-based perspective. Here, morals are right if they are in accord with the commands of a deity (i.e., God). Basically, morality, in this sense, means it is right if commanded by God, and wrong if forbidden by God (Ingram & Parks, 2002; Rachels, 1986).

Where do these commands come from? As you have probably guessed, from books such as the Bible, the Koran, or other sacred texts. Within these texts are rules of right and wrong. And where do the rules come from? They all come from God. According to sacred books, not only is God the creator of the universe and the laws of nature, but God is also the author of moral rules. These moral rules or divine commands are considered universal and independent of culture and personal moral preferences (Rauhut, 2006). Beside all that, they give many people a feeling of security in that they clearly state what is right or wrong (even when you might have hesitations). Therefore, there is a sense of objectivity about God's commands (Rachels, 1986). Finally, and for many, these commands give one a compelling motivation to be moral. If you are good, you reap the rewards of heavenly afterlife; if you are bad, well let's just say that the afterlife will not be pleasant.

As an example of divine command, here a few rules from the Ten Commandments of the Judeo-Christian tradition:

■ You shall honor your mother and father.
■ You shall not commit adultery.

- You shall not steal.
- You shall not bear false witness against your neighbor.
- You shall not covet anything that belongs to your neighbor.

A Few Problems With Divine Command

Despite all the stated strengths of the divine command moral position, it has not escaped criticism. Philosophical thinkers have identified problems with it (Ingram & Parks, 2002). We will briefly identify some of these problems for the sake of perspective.

For one, divine command leaves open the possibility that if God changes his mind as to what is moral, then murder could conceivably be OK. Next, many religious texts contain inconsistencies (for example, in the Bible, God did command Moses to kill a lot of people). Next, ethicists in general try to avoid "might makes right" thinking. Might does not make right for all people in the world. However, God would, by sheer force, impose his form of ethics on us all. In this sense, God can appear similar to an angry father, insisting that one do it his way or else. This flies in the face of the important ethical element of not imposing one's ethics on other people. Finally, divine command is limited. It does not come close to covering all the possible moral issues in life (Ingram & Parks, 2002).

Given the outline and problems, it is now time to begin to think of how you might apply this to everyday addiction ethics. Could there possibly be a fit using this position? You need to measure the weight of addiction ethics judgments you make in light of divine command. If you use it, is your weight a little heavy or too light in terms of your ethical judgments and decisions? On the other hand, you may need to look through the eye of divine command at times to supplement your judgments and decisions.

Divine command is one way to look at morals. But there are other described universal perspectives. The next one maintains that you do not need to rely on divine guidance for your ethics, but rather on the secular.

DEONTOLOGY

If you happen to make your addiction ethics decisions based on what you believe is your duty, then you are utilizing a view called *deontology,* which is a fancy word for duty. The duty position comes with a particularly strong attachment—obligation.

We will get to this and other important elements, but first let's look at deontology from a broad, encompassing perspective. Then we will work our way down through the small, detailed particulars.

One way to get this wide perspective is to consider how people thought about duty throughout the ages. Let's go all the way back to Roman times and a fellow named Cicero. In his last book, *On Duties,* he tried to address a number of difficult problems, including ethics. He had a simple approach to ethical problems—do the right thing. Wrong decisions, while they can give you advantage (such as short-changing a Roman customer by selling poor quality bread), are always wrong. So what is right? Cicero kept it simple. Right, he thought, was what was legal, honest, open, and fair. It meant keeping your word, no matter the consequences, and telling the truth. It meant treating everyone (including slaves and women, who were not afforded equal treatment at that time) similarly. Everyone's humanness gave them the right to be so treated (Van Doren, 1991).

About 18 centuries later, another philosopher came along and explored duty. That 19th-century philosopher's name was Immanuel Kant. He was convinced that compulsory universal ethical laws exist. And he proposed a secular (nondivine) idea of universal morality. He suggested that certain laws simply exist as what he called a priori ideas. According to Kant, there are such moral laws, and he was searching for nothing less than a fundamental moral law.

Rather than base his universal moral laws on sacred books, Kant believed that these laws came from the structure of the human mind, where reason is based. And rather than seek the essence of all moral interpretations, he sought the grounds of morality (Strathern, 1996). In other words, he was not seeking concepts such as "Thou shall not kill," which is a standard of content. He was searching for a framework.

As stated, Kant believed all morality is to be found in reason (Brown, 1996; Christian, 1977; Magee, 1998). If you are going to lead a moral life or make ethical decisions, then, according to Kant, you must act in a rational, conscious, and consistent way (Ingram & Parks, 2002).

Now here is the tough part, or what some would call the inflexible part. When it comes to making universal moral codes (or a universal addiction ethics code), you can't say something is universal and then act differently. Put another way, you can't on the one hand create a set of universal ethical codes with which to run your addiction treatment program, and then make an exception to the rules because you favor a particular client. That would not be rational or consistent. And not being rational or consistent would not fit a universal ethical code.

Your Intent

If that isn't strict enough, your aim, goal, purpose, or *intent* is a central feature in the deontological view. For instance, say you notice that some of your colleagues tend to shave a few minutes off work every now and then. You also notice these very same people are quick to storm into the boss's office if they don't get the promised overtime pay they think is owed to them. Seems like a contradiction on their part, doesn't it? They intend not to be accountable for taking time off but do intend to be paid overtime. If that sounds like a contradiction to you, it is. And Kant has an answer for it. He puts forth two key points that directly link to this example. If you get these points, you pretty much get this ethical view.

1. Only good will (and nothing else but good will) has an ultimate moral value.
2. Moral rules are universal and binding, and apply to all rational beings (rational beings being you and me).

Kant would say your colleagues are not acting with good will. And good will, in Kant's moral framework, is everything.

But wait, we are not done with intent. Now we must put the spotlight on you and your obligation to do the right thing. You saw the behavior of your colleagues (shaving time off of work), so what should you do about it? Kant says your duty and your obligation is to report the infractions. But your intent matters as well. If you report your colleagues just to make yourself look good, that is the wrong intention. You should report them because it is the morally superior act and because it shows your intent to do your duty. Sure, you could wink and say nothing, but that intent would be faulty. And it would betray a basic sense of good will.

Good Will

So we have been talking about good will, but what is it? Essentially, Kant said we should not be judged on what we achieve but on what we *try* to achieve. Good will is the driving motive behind our action. If the motive is good, then the action is good. But that Kantian explanation seems to go in circles for those who want something a little more concrete.

Try this: The theory is that good will is good in itself. Kant firmly believed even the highest virtue can be misused, including the virtues of intelligence, good temperament, or using one's personal money for good (Brown, 1996). Why are these not adequate? Well, intelligence can be used in service of bad deeds, like planning a robbery. A good temperament, such as patience, can be used to wait for the perfect time to do the robbery.

To make this point more understandable, let's consider the element of respect. Think of good will as something that rises above one's self. Think of it as an objective variable, where good will commands recognition and a commendation for doing what is good in and of itself, and in Kant's view, we simply command it of ourselves (Brown, 1996).

Let's try this. Go back to the example of your colleagues shaving time off of work. Kant would say, Do you know how you could really claim good will is good? You could claim it if what you do could be applied to all the people in the world. Or, to put it another way, a will is good if it acts on motives that apply to all humanity (Rauhut, 2006). With this in mind, we can now test your morality for good will. So would you want your colleagues behavior, or better yet what prompted it, to be something that could be applied to all humanity? If your answer is no, then you are beginning to understand good will and the importance of intent. Good will is the driving force behind all intent.

Once you understand this good will thing, what do you do with it? This is where deontology really gets interesting. You do your duty.

Your Duty

A few paragraphs back we said that deontology is a duty-based, universal, and absolute approach to ethics. In this view, rules are meant to be followed. There are no excuses for not following them. As it happens, among Kant's most basic absolute rules are the following: always tell the truth, keep your promises, develop your potential, and don't commit suicide (Ingram & Parks, 2002; Rauhut, 2006). (Some people would say these are not a bad set of moral rules.)

It is your duty to follow such rules. This is a critical piece of deontology and will help you determine if you tend to use this ethical position as your default addiction ethics judgment mode. Duty means doing what is required of you whether you want to or not, or even when you face difficult ethical decisions (Ingram & Parks, 2002). Duty is a principle to behave in a certain way regardless of the consequences, and, whether you like it or not, it may trump the greater good or good of the majority (Baggini & Fosl, 2007).

Now, Kant made one little differentiation of duty. He noted that some people act in *accordance* with duty, and some act with the *motive* of duty (Kenny, 1994). For example, a goodhearted rich person who delights in making others happy by donating his money could be said to act in accordance with duty. Applying this to the addiction field, it could be the counselor who happens to enjoy hanging out with clients during her spare time. Now, there is no argument that these types of duty do produce good outcomes. The goodhearted fellow's money is certainly making people happy, and it could be argued that the addiction counselor is helping clients practice their sober interaction skills. But they don't have worth in Kant's eyes because they are only in accord or in harmony with duty. They were not done from the motive of duty. In the addiction example, acting out of a motive of duty might be the counselor spending time with a client even though she had errands to run or other obligations. Acting that way would be from duty.

Remember that Kant thought it was good will that drives duty. Your desire (intent) to do good is the thing that counts, or what is called *good-in-itself*, and Kant didn't believe in doing good with anything else but good will in mind. Not even doing good with honor in mind, or with courage in mind, is true good will. Why? Because virtues like honor or courage or intelligence can be corrupted and make things worse. How can noble virtues such as honor and courage be corrupted? Well, you can have a very courageous, honorable, and intelligent assassin. Or, you can have a very courageous addiction counselor who uses that courage as a way to risk boundary violations with a client.

Even the intent to bring happiness can be corrupted. Let's consider an addiction counselor who has a client wash his car. He believes that the boundary violation makes both him and the client happy in that the counselor gets free labor (car washed), and the client supposedly learns satisfaction from doing a job well done in a sober fashion. However, happy, in this case, doesn't make things moral and can lead to corrupt ethics decisions. The problem is that, according to Kant, the counselor acted from self-interest—not duty. One's duty should be done from a reasoned perspective of doing what is right and not from trying to indulge a feeling of what is right. The latter perspective is subjective, not objective nor universal. True duty is done outside of one's best personal interest (Brown, 1996). So Kant would say you have a duty to perform.

We're almost done with this, so hang in there. Don't consider duty as something that is imposed on you, such as a set of state ethical guidelines, which you must obey or risk being punished if you don't. Duty, in Kant's definition, presupposes that you know what is right and wrong, and you therefore expect yourself to do what is right. Kant felt that ethics that are imposed on you (as in religious rules or state ethical codes) without your reasoned input are not really ethics at all.

The manifestation of duty is the *categorical imperative,* and we do what it commands. It is a compulsory rule, and it clearly states: Act only according to that maxim by which you could will it as universal law, to never treat others as mere means to ends but always ends in themselves (Baggini & Fosl, 2007; Ingram & Parks, 2002; Roberson & Garratt, 1999). So, when it comes time for a moral choice, simply ask, "What if everybody did that?" Would the act be a reasonable universal law for all the people in the world? Would you want all people to do what you just did? As an example, imagine that as an addiction counselor you begin to pad your time at work so that you can claim compensatory time in order to get time off you really didn't earn. Would such an act be OK for all other addiction counselors to do?

And all of this gets us back to good intentions. According to Kant, it is better to act with good will and have something turn out bad than to start out with bad intentions that just happen to turn out well. Doing duty driven from good will is all that counts for Kant. Folks who do their duty for duty's sake do what is right because it is right.

For example, say your program has a policy to notify a client's probation officer about any positive urine analysis test, which will likely get the client sent back to prison. Some addiction counselors would send a client back to prison because of a positive urine analysis because it is their duty to keep the bargain they made with the probation officer. It is the honest thing to do. They are acting out of good will toward doing their duty. Note that it may not result in the best outcome for the client, given the negative experiences that the client will likely encounter in prison.

Others might send a client back to prison not just because it is their duty, but because deep inside they feel frustrated with the client and see this as a way to get back at him and get him off their caseload for a time. So, in both examples, the addiction counselors send the client to prison: but one acts out of good will, and the other has tarnished reasons. So, from

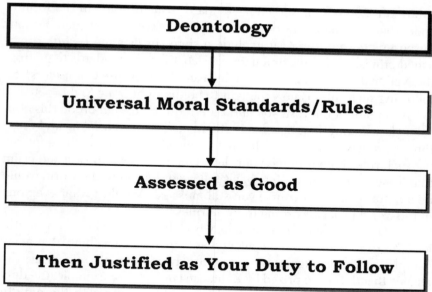

Figure 5.3 Deontology summary.

this point of view, we have to really examine our intentions (Ingram & Parks, 2002).

Behind this imperative (requirement) is Kant's entreaty to think about your ethics. That's the heart of the imperative. The imperative is an obligation imposed on all of us that goes beyond our personal desires (Ingram & Parks, 2002). It is a method to help us figure out how to act. It doesn't say act this way or that but presses us to figure it out for ourselves (hence, the secular element). See Figure 5.3 for a visual summary.

Some Strengths and Weakness of Deontology

A stand out strength of this view is that it provides a clear and unambiguous set of moral rules (Marinoff, 2003). The categorical imperative is the central rule. So, in terms of addiction ethics, you need to ask yourself: In terms of an addiction ethics decision, would you want it to be adopted by all addiction counselors? If the answer is yes, then you are adhering to this maxim.

Another strength of this ethical perspective is that it is straightforward. When in doubt about an addiction ethics issue, you can always follow a rationally derived set of standards or rules that tell you what to do

(Marinoff, 2003). Our addiction standards usually come in the form of codes that were rationally derived and are now considered good. For our purposes, those criteria can include a state certification board's established ethical standards, or a national slate of such standards (e.g., from the National Association of Alcoholism and Drug Abuse Counselors). So following such rules is now thought to be the right thing to do.

As a point of interest, you and I are required to sign off on this ethical code when we first become certified addiction counselors and every time we renew. That process has now evolved to the point where following such rules is considered your duty. One might extrapolate and claim that if most addiction professionals followed the codes, the world would be a better place. (Of course you still must ask: Would I want everyone in the world to act according to these rules?)

A glaring weakness of deontology is its black-and-white view of ethics. This perspective does not allow shades of gray or flexibility that many complex addiction dilemmas may require. In addition, there is always the chance that duties, so prized by Kant, can conflict. For example, the duty to protect the confidentiality of others might conflict with the duty to save the lives of others. (Think of a situation where you are duty-bound to maintain the confidentiality of a client who is HIV-positive, but you know that the client is actively having sex with others and not informing them of his condition.) Interestingly, this position almost demands too much perfection from humans. Most of us do not do perfect well. Finally, deontology does not allow the consequences of our action to be of ethical significance (a bad outcome does not matter if it was the product of good intentions). This is something we will address in the next section.

UTILITARIANISM

Utilitarianism is a very different moral theory than deontology. The history of this moral theory begins in 19th-century England with a fellow named Jeremy Bentham. In his time, he saw what he considered the injustice of certain laws and morals. He felt the technocrats of the time were dehumanizing society with no benefit to culture or community (Turnbull, 1998). He saw actions that did no harm being condemned, while actions that did great harm went unpunished (Vaughn, 2008). All this, he felt, did not make any logical sense, nor did it have any scientific foundation. Moreover, Bentham felt that it was nonsense to claim English laws were good just because people said so (Roberson & Garratt, 1999). Essentially, utilitarianism grew out of suffering. Bentham proposed a morality that was both practical and could socially reform the thinking of the day. His moral position was a radical departure from the traditional theories of the time. It put pressure on the government of the day to justify itself by contributing the greatest good to the greatest number. He insisted that the government justify its actions based on their *utility* (usefulness) and how much pain or pleasure a moral action would ultimately produce. The position eventually became know as *utilitarianism* (Barad & Robertson, 2000; Roberson & Garratt, 1999).

This is a moral theory that comes in a couple of flavors. These varying points of view all fit under the broad category of *consequentialism.* Simply put, judgments such as whether an action is right or wrong or good or bad are based on the outcomes or consequences of the action (Baggini & Fosl, 2007; Ingram & Parks, 2002).

A good way to understand utilitarianism is to think of it as a method that presses you to choose between two moral options, and then favor the one that gives the most happiness. A historical example might help; think of women's suffrage. There was once great debate in the United States around women's right to vote. One side argued not to allow women the right to vote. This created a lot of unhappiness among women (if not a few men) at the time. The other side argued in favor of women's right to vote. After protesting, marching, and political action, an amendment to the Constitution was finally passed. It created positive consequences (because half the population of the country could now vote), which created more net happiness. From a utilitarian perspective, granting women the right to vote created the most happiness, provided the most well-being, and thus was the moral and ethical thing to do.

An example from the addiction field can be seen in the same light. For centuries, there was a strong stigma associated with alcoholism (there still is to a certain extent). Society at large openly and blatantly shunned those who drank excessively. Often alcoholics were not given the proper medical care as a result. That situation created a lot of unhappy alcoholics who were trying to get help but who found no place to turn. In 1955, however, the American Medical Association proclaimed that alcoholism was a disease. This change in perception began to finally open doors for alcoholics wanting help, and treatment options grew sharply within a decade. The change provided many clients with treatment and a second chance where none had existed before. This increase in treatment brought about more net positive consequences and made many people happy.

Two Parts to Utilitarianism

It was noted earlier that utilitarianism comes in a couple of flavors. One such position is called *act utilitarianism*. It states that no act is right or wrong in and of itself, which at first sounds odd. However, act utilitarianism claims that the good or bad act depends on the consequence it brings about. If the outcome is good, you can say you did the right thing. If the outcome is bad, you did the wrong thing.

The other flavor is called *rule utilitarianism*. It is very simple and states that morality should still be about obeying moral rules, particularly if such rules have shown themselves to bring the most happiness to the most people (Roberson & Garratt, 1999).

Other Definitions of Utilitarianism

The previous descriptions are the traditional definition of utilitarianism. But there are different ways of describing the theory, which might provide some more clarity. For example:

- Another way of stating act utilitarianism is that it is the consequences of an action that make the action right, not whether the action broke a rule or violated a moral principle (Vaughn, 2008).
- Another way of saying this is that if happiness is maximized by a particular action, then regardless of other concerns, the action is judged morally right (Vaughn, 2008).
- Put simply, the end justifies the means (Vaughn, 2008).

Consider that when utilitarianism was developed, it arguably caused a groundswell that inspired reformers to go after slavery, eliminate child labor, and work toward women's rights (Vaughn, 2008). Such reformations clearly maximized the happiness of these groups. That something can cause good consequences, even despite the moral standards of the day, is at the very core of utilitarianism.

Try This On

We want to make the philosophical explanations a bit more personal. Seeing these explanations at a close-up level can bring a dry moral theory to life. Perhaps you can relate to it better. Remember, all we are doing is just trying on the theory to see how it fits. Plus, we are trying to determine if you discover that this is the view you favor when you make ethical judgments.

First, picture yourself making an addiction ethics decision from the utilitarian view. Say you take an ethical behavior, such as staying late at work. This action might well make a number of clients (e.g., 10 people) happy in that they could get a chance to talk about the day's treatment. This action would clearly be a utilitarian action. However, your spouse or partner (just one person) might be unhappy. What, in your judgment, is the ethical thing to do?

Next, try to judge others from the utilitarian view. Consider that you work in an inpatient program and your staff decides to discharge one person because the client has been disruptive and problematic. Many other clients favor this decision and believe the action will bring more peace and stability to the entire unit. The individual to be discharged will, in all likelihood, begin using drugs again. In the process, the client may well suffer many more consequences of addiction. But many others would be happy. What, in your judgment, is the ethical thing to do?

This scenario highlights some issues with the utilitarianism position.

Utilitarianism: A Few Problems

- One problem for this ethical position is that it is too demanding. For example, you should never rest on a Saturday afternoon when you could make more people happy by spending time with the homeless, writing a letter to your parents, or an endless number of other such activities (Rauhut, 2006).
- In addition, whatever action you take at the time may not, in retrospect, be the act that causes the most possible happiness. That act can and will be open to a future assessment that could outweigh the credence of the present ethical decision (Rauhut, 2006).
- Within this view, consider an action that makes an individual happy yet infringes on another's rights. Consider as an example a peeping tom who secretly takes photos of others for his own benefit but does so without being detected. He never shows the photos to others or uses them to gain financial reward. According to the utilitarian logic, no one got hurt, and someone became happy. However, rights were breached.
- Utilitarianism redirects attention from personal convictions and values to outside assessment. Sometimes it might be better to act

out of conviction and virtue than what would bring the most happiness (Thompson, 2003).

This last point brings us to the next big moral position.

VIRTUE ETHICS

Here we step into the realm of moral character. Here the agent (you) is the focus of moral judgment and action. Instead of saying stealing is wrong because it violates a religious law, or some duty, or would bring unhappiness to others, virtue ethics states that stealing is wrong because it corrupts character (Rauhut, 2006). And this corruption of character is seen to be more fundamental than the other core ethical foundations mentioned in this chapter. Essentially, the key question in virtue ethics is this: "What kind of person should I be?" This can extend to the question of what is a good life or what is a life that is well lived (Solomon, 1993)? These questions date to Greek philosophers such as Socrates, who defined virtue as doing the right thing, and Aristotle, who may have been the first to systematically spell out virtues. As varied as the definitions of virtue are, it may be safe to say virtue boils down to a desirable character (Solomon, 1993).

Virtue ethics is not about looking for a universal moral set of rules or ethical standards, as in the other theories. Instead, it is directed at moral character that is perceived as admirable. Admirable characteristics are those that people have internalized as virtues. Virtue, it is felt, adds to what is considered a moral life. Virtues are cultivated and generally stand without question. Yet virtues are not universal. Each culture and society values particular virtues and passes them down to the next generation (Gazzaniga, 2008). Virtues and vices have changed over the centuries and across cultures.

The mark of a virtuous person is that the learned virtues become engrained in one's character (Solomon, 1993). Meet someone with such character and, according to virtue ethics, it will soon become evident that he or she has virtue.

In terms of addiction recovery, many of the virtues to be discussed are recommended by various 12-step groups as attributes or mechanisms that assist the recovery process. On the other hand, the vices, to be discussed later, are seen to contribute to ongoing addiction problems if not relapse. Talk to anyone committed to a 12-step program and you will hear self-talk peppered with conversation of virtue and vice.

In terms of addiction ethics, counselors and other addiction professionals are expected to maintain if not foster certain virtues. Should addiction professionals drift to the dark side (develop vices), professional
ethical problems are seen to follow. It may be language that gets us to
the heart of virtue by the use of terms such as *admiration* and *disgust*
(Solomon, 1993).

Examples of Virtue and Vice

There are a number of virtues and vices, and the reader will immediately
recognize them. The following list, while not extensive, presents some common virtues and vices. We often use some virtue or vice to judge addiction
ethics problems or make ethical decisions. You are asked to personally examine the list as you did all the previous ethical models. First, you need to
assess the weight of your potential judgment in light of virtue. Do you find
your use of virtues weighs a little heavy or perhaps a little light in terms of
an addiction ethics decision? Second, you may need to look through the
lens of virtue ethics to round out and complete your conclusions.

So here are some of the more traditional virtues (in no particular
order of importance) (Rauhut, 2006):

- **Honesty** or integrity, truthfulness, candor, openness
- **Civility** or courtesy, respect, consideration
- **Fairness** or equality, evenhandedness, justice
- **Compassion** or care, concern, kindness
- **Dependability** or reliability, steadiness
- **Courage** or bravery, nerve, valor
- **Generosity** or kindness, charity, bigheartedness
- **Sense of justice** or fairness, impartiality, evenhandedness
- **Good temperament** or levelheadedness, even-temperedness,
  calmness
- **Loyalty** or trustworthiness, dependability, devotion
- **Humility** or modesty, meekness
- **Moderation** or self-control, self-restraint, temperance

Here are some of the more traditional vices (in no particular order
of importance) (Rauhut, 2006):

- **Anger** or irritation, fury, rage
- **Selfishness** or self-centeredness, egotism, self-absorption

- **Envy** or desire, covetousness, jealousy
- **Sloth** or laziness, indolence, apathy
- **Lust** or desire, hunger, longing
- **Greed** or gluttony, avarice, self-indulgence
- **Covetousness** or greed, cupidity
- **Rudeness** or impoliteness, discourtesy, disrespect
- **Dishonesty** or deceit, duplicity, trickery
- **Pride** or conceit, arrogance, overconfidence

Virtue Ethics Applied to Addiction Ethics

We can connect virtue ethics to addiction ethics by asking a few questions raised by this perspective (Thompson, 2003). For example, do we humans have a fixed essence in terms of virtues and vices? If so, how much control do we have over our actions? This last question has a direct impact on addiction ethics judgments. Do some of the previously listed vices contribute to the onset of addiction? Do some contribute to relapse? Would it be ethical to teach some of the virtues in modern treatment programs?

Virtue ethics could not be complete without a brief discussion of role models. People who display most or all the virtues previously listed are often seen as role models. While up for argument, the role model list often includes the likes of Socrates, Jesus Christ, Mohammed, Buddha, Abraham Lincoln, Mother Theresa, and Dr. Martin Luther King Jr. Who might you add? And what set of virtues or lack of vices affect who you would include on this list?

Problems With Virtue Ethics

No discussion of virtues would be complete without some mention of virtues gone mad. For example, while civility is a virtue, too much civility is not good, as in offering civility to someone or something that does not warrant it (e.g., Hitler). When would the other virtues become vices? How might that affect addiction ethics judgments and actions?

There are some limiting points to be made about the virtue ethics position. For one, a person can be downright nasty and not violate anyone's basic rights. You could be courageous and still be a mean person (Ingram & Parks, 2002). Moreover, would following virtues be the best thing to do all the time? Would it be best for someone who is so caring for others that she ends up not taking care of her own needs, or for someone who is so afraid of hurting someone else's feelings that she never stops them when they do bad things to her?

Sometimes virtues conflict. For example, telling the truth when a client breaks a small rule in treatment and then discharging her shows the virtue of honesty, yet giving her a second chance might be the more generous or moderate choice. Finally, virtues can be misused, as in thieves being courageous and temperate in order to do their job more efficiently (Brown, 1996). So is it good to be good? Or do different situations, addiction ethics included, need different virtues? Think it through.

THE LEAST YOU NEED TO KNOW

The major ethical positions include the following:

- Divine command—Morals are right if they are in accord with God's commands.
- Deontology—A secular set of universal moral standards exists. If such a rule is assumed to be good, then it is your duty to follow.
- Utilitarianism—If happiness is maximized by a particular action, then regardless of other concerns, the action is judged morally right.
- Virtue ethics—What kind of person should I be?
- There are a host of moral theories to choose from when it comes time to make your moral judgments and decisions. This chapter asked you to assess which felt most comfortable to you. Once you have established this position, you are to acknowledge this as a possible core moral stance, and each time you judge an addiction ethics position, carefully weigh that influence on your judgment and decision.

A Few Other Ethical Theories

We now come to a smattering of other ethical theories. While each discussion is not as in-depth as in the last chapter, they are listed for the same two major reasons: to give you a broad ethical perspective and to allow you to discover which view you tend to use when you judge addiction ethics problems.

SOCIAL CONTRACT THEORY

Some theorists have suggested that we all abide by certain rules. On the one hand, such rules limit the things we can do. However, the limitations still give us a measure of security and freedom and allow us to live together reasonably well (Thompson, 2003). Back in the 16th century, Thomas Hobbes took this basic idea and expanded on it. He put forth the notion that the people who live in a certain country and their ruler should agree to a contract. The ruler would protect the people (thus giving them safety) and the people would accept the authority of the ruler (following the rules so all can live reasonably well together). A neat and clean contract.

There have been some modifications of this idea over the centuries. Jean-Jacques Rousseau claimed that rather than be forced by society to submit to a contract, we impose limits on ourselves (Solomon, 1993). Others have argued that social contracts have to be fair. No one group should have to bear all the burdens while another enjoys most of the benefits. We are all interdependent for our common well-being. What we have today is something like an ongoing contract process that understands our mutual duties as citizens so we call all live reasonably well together (Ingram & Parks, 2002). This social contract can be summed up as: I'll keep my obligations if you keep yours.

So how would contract theory apply to addiction ethics? That may best be answered by asking a few questions. For example, how do we assess and judge someone who breaks a social contract, such as taking undo advantage of others, which some people with an active addiction do? If we assume that people are responsible for keeping their contracts, what do we do when they don't? How are we to bring order to treatment programs when certain individuals do not keep their end of the bargain?

Now measure the weight of a potential addiction judgment in light of social contract theory. Is your weight a little heavy or too light in terms of your ethical judgments and decisions? Second, you may need to look through the eye of social contract theory to supplement your judgments and decisions.

FEMINIST ETHICS

All the ethical views discussed so far (and those to come) were created by men. These ethical views, if you haven't noticed, often have an absolute tone to them. But is this the only way to understand ethics? Could there be another way, perhaps a female moral perspective? Some feminists assert there is, and it centers not on absolute rules of conduct or on rules derived purely by rationality (Thompson, 2003). It centers instead on relatedness and an ethics of care. It prioritizes relationships and how they will be affected by certain actions. The key moral obligation in this ethical perspective is to avoid harm and help people (MacKinnon, 2004).

Feminists would have us question the whole idea of impartiality in situations such as who to save from a burning building. If it were your children, the right thing to do would be to go get them. There is nothing wrong with letting personal considerations weigh in on an ethical dilemma (Ingram & Parks, 2002). For our purposes, consider these elements when it comes time to make addiction ethics judgments and decisions.

ETHICAL EGOISM

This view may cause you to do more than the usual self-examination when it comes to your addiction ethics judgments and actions. *Psychological egoism* would have you believe that all our actions and judgments stem from a motive of self-interest (Ingram & Parks, 2002). But the *ethical egoists* go one step farther and say we should always act in our own best interests. In fact, we have an obligation to act in the way that best benefits ourselves (Thompson, 2003). In this perspective, you don't have duties to others. You have one duty, and it is to yourself. If individuals really matter, then they shouldn't sacrifice for others or the common good. So altruism is out the window. Sounds selfish, doesn't it?

Well, let's look at it through the eyes of the egoist. Egoists would not tell you to stop helping little old ladies across the street or not to help your neighbor paint his house. They would say, however, that you do such altruistic acts purely to make yourself feel better—so why not just admit it (Ingram & Parks, 2002)?

Moreover, egoists would claim that charity and altruism are essentially offensive and paternalistic. In terms of paternalism, people don't like having others decide what is best for them. So, the egoists suggest, we as individuals know what's best in terms of our self-interests. Anyway, if we try to do things for others, we often get it wrong. So it's best to let folks act for themselves. But we can be of assistance, as long as we admit that our altruism is just a way to make ourselves feel better.

Yet a big problem with this view is that it pretty much sees the world as self versus others. Moreover, feeling good about doing something nice for others could be seen as a benefit of leading a good life. Finally, all of us at one time or another may benefit from—or desperately need—charity or altruism (Ingram & Parks, 2002).

How does this apply to addiction ethics? It forces addiction professionals to deeply examine *why* they act ethically. In addition, it forces addiction professionals to examine why they choose this field as a career and what weight they place on making ethical decisions that might ultimately make them feel better about themselves.

EXISTENTIALISM

A key existential thinker was Jean-Paul Sartre (Solomon, 1993). Sartre took Kant's insistence on personal responsibility to extremes. Sartre would have individuals not transfer moral responsibility onto anyone but one's self. We are the ones who make our decisions and choices and we have to live with them. If one holds this view, many of the prevailing views of addiction and treatment might have to be rethought. According to Sartre, an individual with an addiction cannot shift responsibility for that addiction but rather must shoulder it squarely him- or herself. While Sartre does not imply that such individuals be demonized, he certainly implies that an individual must take full responsibility for his or her actions.

JUSTICE AND RIGHTS-BASED APPROACHES

These are two ethical viewpoints that will be very briefly stated:

- *Fairness or justice*—When making an ethical decision, which decision or action will treat people fairly and equally? Or, if people are treated unequally, which decision or action would treat the people involved proportionately and fairly?
- *Rights-based approach*—Which ethical action or decision respects the rights of everyone involved? In other words, what ethical decision is fair to all individuals in the ethical situation?

RELATIVISM/SUBJECTIVISM

We save this view for the last. It is a position that can certainly generate contention, hence it needs a bit more explanation. First, we will examine what it is, and then discuss its flaws, and finally try to take a few points away from the discussion.

Ethical relativism or *subjectivism* is not so much a specific theory of what's right and wrong as has been defined in many of the preceding positions. It's not that kind of theory. Rather, it's more of a claim about the nature or spirit of good and bad. That claim centers on accepting moral positions on personal (subjective) opinion or cultural perspectives (Ingram & Parks, 2002). The core of this position rejects the idea that there is one absolute and universal moral rule that applies to all people at all times (Baggini & Fosl, 2007). According to the relativists, moral and ethical beliefs are clearly not held in isolation. They are influenced by the system in which you live. And those systems vary from one region of the earth to another (Wolpert, 2006).

While there is much debate on this position, ethical subjectivism has been criticized for suggesting that moral views of things are based on individual feelings, nothing more (Rachels, 1986). Some describe the relativist as the ultimate skeptic in that he or she is committed to the view that there are no real ethical statements for positions (Rauhut, 2006; Steward & Blocker, 1982). This stance leaves only one position—anything is permissible (Marinoff, 2003), because there are no truths in ethics (Steward & Blocker, 1982). Technically, ethical relativism is a set of morals relative to the speaker or the speaker's culture. Different ethical standards are correct for different groups of people (MacKinnon, 2004; Steward & Blocker, 1982).

If you are a relativist, you essentially back the position that no one ethical view is better than another. Now, this is important. Relativism does not assume there are no standards at all; just that no one view is superior to another. This perception of multiple sets of moral standards implies a sense of equality (Baggini & Fosl, 2003). This equality stance may arguably stand as one of relativism's better points. It is also arguably why liberals tend to favor the view, while conservatives tend to feel more comfortable with absolute sets of rules. So this should warn us to be careful not to make addiction ethics decisions with politics in mind.

An overall argument adapted from Steward and Blocker (1982) for ethical relativism runs something like this:

Different people have different ethical judgments and decisions.

If different people make different ethical judgments and decisions, then those different people often believe in different ethical standards.

Therefore,

Different people often believe different ethical standards, and different ethical standards are correct for the different people (∴ ethical relativism is true).

Certainly, this argument is up for debate; but it illustrates the central point of relativism.

Relativism has a close cousin—*postmodernism*. This concept insists that there really isn't a real world out there. That's right: there is no objectivity. Rather, truth is completely arbitrary and constructed by unspoken agreement. Moreover, our thinking and styles of communication are intimately linked with language, and that makes everything merely text or words. And if everything is just language, we can make up things to suit ourselves as to what is real and what it not (Buchanan, 2007). Why point out this last connection? One needs to see the web of arguments that surround relativism. British historian Geoffrey Elton maintains that this trend is like intellectual crack, it allows anything to go, and frees anyone who uses it from the responsibility to think coherently (Buchanan, 2007). If that is to be believed, then freedom from coherent thought is problematic for ethics in general and addiction ethics in particular.

Problems With Relativism

A lot of people who espouse the relativist position like to assert that a particular theory or moral principle "is true for me." As if that magically transforms mere belief into a true belief (Woodhouse, 1994). If that were so, we in general wouldn't need evidence or proof, and most so-called truths would be based on whim (Woodhouse, 1994). Such a state of so-called reasoning does not make for an ethical standard by which you and I can judge addiction issues. Essentially, moral values should be open to examination, evidence, and reason so they can be modified (Kurtz, 2007). Relativism would frown on such a proposal, and that is one argument not to support it.

Take this line of thought to the next level, where certain supporters of subjectivism imply that my beliefs and opinions are not subject to rational argument (Curtler, 2004). If you really believe that your ethical point of view is beyond argument, then you believe that there are no good reasons to examine evidence or sound judgment for the purpose of revising one's opinion, because no one view is better (Hare, 2009).

Second, isn't there more to beliefs than mere personal feelings? If so, then we have to account for rational thought. Have there been situations where you caused emotional pain to others, and hence learned to be considerate of their needs in the future? Or have you not seen others hurt morally by some act and then learned from that act? If so, you have used thought and rationality. Moreover, you have been taught how to act morally from your family, religious upbringing if any, and community.

Third, just because folks have different beliefs does not mean that ethical truth is absent from their different views.

Fourth, just because there are different ethical views does not preclude arguments being created to establish positions for and against some personal or cultural standard. For example, the whipping of alcoholics may be considered ethical in some countries that have an absolute rule against the use of alcohol, but it may be considered unethical in other parts of the world, where whipping someone for having a disease is seen as unacceptable corporal punishment.

In an effort to be unbiased and respectful of cultural differences, many people erroneously equate respect with uncritical acceptance. While it is important to be respectful of other views, it is also important to critically examine positions when they collide or promote unethical behavior (Johnson & Ridley, 2008).

Fifth, if you believe that anything goes, you will have problems reconciling various ideas. For instance, the subjectivist would have to hold that alcoholics be treated as people with a disease (according to the medical model) *and* cast out as sinners (according to the moral view).

Curtler (2004) claims that relativism doesn't get us anywhere. It advances nothing. It allows for all unethical behavior under the guise of "well it's their culture, it's their opinion, and so we shouldn't interfere, because that would be wrong." The question (and there is always a question) to ask when we encounter these kinds of statements is what is wrong with questioning ethical acts, no matter what the opinion or no matter what the culture?

Now if those are not problems enough, how do relativists justify conflicting ethical claims? What is the process such proponents lay out?

What is troubling are the people who glibly use this position not to judge, when in fact they should. Some in the human services and addiction fields, when faced with ethical situations, will state something to the effect, "Who is to say what's right and what's wrong?" (Steward & Blocker, 1982). And that statement often morphs into, "Who are we to judge?" Then no judgment takes place. This is an example of taking an extreme respectful stance and using it in a careless, thoughtless manner.

In addition, there are those who sit on the sidelines and observe unethical behavior and say nothing because they are frightened or scared to be tagged with a label (racist, sexist, etc.). They have been intimidated into silence by the rhetoric of the name-calling relativist crowd.

Curtler (2004) lays out some interesting ideas regarding relativism. One idea is not to fall into the relativism trap, which simply would reduce all ethical claims to personal and cultural opinion. Second, if one is to dissect an ethical conclusion, there needs to be a good set of reasons and justifications—not merely "the reasons that satisfy me." Reasons and justifications should have enough appeal to persuade many people.

Arguments need justifications. Yet the relativist is sure to insist that all reasons and justifications are relative. What do you think?

Finally, conflicting ethical claims cannot both be justified. If indeed ethical claims do conflict with another, one or both must be false. For example, if the claim that dual relationships in addiction counseling is ethically wrong is correct, then the conflicting claim, that dual relationships in addiction counseling are permissible, cannot be justified.

Before we leave this section, I'd like to add a few sentences on the favorite relativist ploy of imposition. Relativists are eager to suggest that critical thinking is out to impose values on other cultures. Well, that's not quite true. Critical thinking would stop being critical thinking if it imposed a position. It would morph into a declarative closed-minded position of telling people what to do. And while some may use critical thinking in that way, it is not now or ever been the position of critical thinking to impose anything, save building solid arguments and avoiding fallacies. Nothing could be more open-minded than the principles outlined by critical thinking.

So what is one to do given this discussion? Baggini and Fosl (2003) offer the idea that when it comes time to make an ethical decision, or in our case an addiction ethics decision, one needs to make clear which position, be it relativism or any others, one is using. Just state it outright. Critical thinking would add that you need to make sure you shore up your choice of an ethical position with a good argument.

Reasons to Use Relativism

Despite the problems listed above, Pinker (2002) points out that relativists attack objectivity and truth not for high-minded philosophical reasons but as the best way to attack social injustices such as racism, sexism, and so forth. The belief is that much of today's problems are due to socially constructed categories (such as gender, race, masculinity versus femininity, etc.) that typically stereotype and lead to prejudice.

With that, might there be some advantages for actually using a relativist position? A big one, perhaps, has to do with our growing pluralist society. Relativism might offer advantages or tolerance for clients who have different cultural perspectives. That is, using the relativism approach with a client who breached a program rule might be warranted in some cases. What would be the morally right thing to do? I don't know. But I would strongly suggest you use all your critical thinking faculties to come to a decision. (See chapter 11 for illustrations.)

THE LEAST YOU NEED TO KNOW

The major ethical positions in this chapter included the following:

- Social contract theory—I'll keep my obligations if you keep yours.
- Feminist ethical theory—Ethical decisions are to be based on care and on principles that avoid harm and help people.
- Ethical egoism—We should always act in our self-interest.
- Existentialism—We should not transfer moral responsibility onto anyone but ourselves. We are the ones who make our decisions and choices and have to live with them.
- Fairness or justice—What action taken, when it comes time to actually make an ethical decision, would treat people fairly and equally?
- Rights-based approach—Which ethical action or decision respects the rights of everyone involved?
- Relativism—Morality is relative to each individual and culture, and we can't make universal moral claims.
- There are a host of moral theories to choose from when it comes time to make your moral judgments and decisions. The chapter asked you to assess which felt most comfortable to you. Once you have established this position, you are to acknowledge this as a possible core moral stance, and each time you judge an addiction ethical position, carefully weigh that influence on your judgment and decision.

7 Theory Application Time

It is now time to apply the various theories we have discussed to addiction ethics. Don't panic. You can do this. This chapter will address one addiction ethics issue as seen through the eyes of the different ethical positions listed in chapters 5 and 6. While reading, keep in mind that it may be difficult to apply broad ethical views to specific problems. However, their usefulness lies in the fact that they provide general avenues to guide one's thinking. That is the major goal of this chapter.

This exercise has several advantages over traditional discussions of addiction ethics. For one, it is a novel way to assess addiction ethics issues. For another, it allows you to see and understand a bit of the practical side of the ethical theories that were just reviewed. Next, it may heighten your natural propensity to assess and judge addiction ethics problems. Recall that part of our ongoing mission is the self-exploration of your ethics, and that includes finding out which ethical theory you favor. Finally, you are encouraged to do some serious thinking here. That means comparing and contrasting how various ethical models differ in their interpretation of addiction ethics. This is in keeping with the book's theme of encouraging you to really *think*.

MORAL DECISIONS BASED ON DIFFERENT PERSPECTIVES

The Situation

A client you really like and who is doing rather well in recovery recently relapsed or, we could say, lapsed. Following his discharge, he was running errands and ran into some old friends who were smoking marijuana. They pestered him just to take a hit. After 15 or so frustrating minutes of saying no, he gave in and took a few hits. He quickly realized the error of his behavior and immediately left this situation and called you (his counselor) to report the incident. He is contrite and sorry. However, the client is on probation. His probation officer (PO), who runs his caseload by the book, wants session updates on this client's condition, especially any relapsing. The PO has made it clear he will revoke the client's probation if the client is found breaching the no drug or alcohol conditions of his probation. The client begs you not to send him back to prison. He has a job lined up and wants to provide for his wife and infant daughter.

The Dilemma

If you disclose the information, there is a high probability the PO will send the client back to prison, which you see as not being particularly helpful in this case. Pleading the client's case may be an option, but that approach has rarely worked with this PO, who is not known for his tolerance. The dilemma is: Do you report the incident or not?

DIFFERENT ETHICAL PERSPECTIVES ON THIS SITUATION

Divine Command

The centerpiece of the divine command perspective is that morals are right if they are in accord with God's commands. In order to assess what is God's command, this perspective would insist that you consult books (preferably religious books) to find what passage would best apply to this situation. In addition, divine command would entreat you to look at your state and national codes for guidance. From this perspective, one of these books or codes would certainly provide you with the guidance you seek. It may well insist that of all the things you might do, do not lie to the PO. Yet at the same time a guiding principle for many a religion is to be merciful.

Deontology

The deontology perspective (Kant) lists the following parameters for its ethics:

- Always act from a sense of duty, not according to it. Act not because duty requires you to act in certain way, but because of duty itself. In other words, if you act because duty requires it, such an action could well involve acting out of self-interest. It may look like you are doing the right thing, but you may well have alternative motives, which are not pure. (Human nature is rarely pure.) Kant would want your ethical intentions to be pure; you should not act according to what the action might accomplish for you (Barad & Robertson, 2000).
- One overcomes one's feelings in order to do one's duty.
- Personal feelings have no place in moral obligations.
- Be concerned with the right conduct and do so rationally.
- An action done with duty has moral worth—perhaps the greatest moral worth, according to Kant.
- From the deontology position, you as an ethical addiction professional have a sense of duty/obligation for good, so you have no other choice but to disclose the drug use to the client's PO.
- Lastly, this position asks, would you want other addiction counselors in the world to follow along with the method by which you made your decision in this case?

Utilitarianism

The utilitarianism perspective (Bentham) lists the following parameters for its ethics:

- You must justify your decision by its utility (usefulness) and through its contribution to the greatest good for the greatest number of people (Barad & Robertson, 2000).
- Actions are judged as right or wrong according to their consequences.

- Furthermore, there needs to be a favorable balance of pleasure over pain.
- Right actions will have the best consequences (so you have to ask the question: Would sending this guy back to prison result in the best consequence for him?).
- Follow whatever rule brings about the greatest good and least amount of harm for the most people. (By sending this guy back to prison, would that be considered the greatest good? Would such an action promote the general welfare of all involved?)

The Virtue Ethics Perspective

Recall that the guiding principle of virtue ethics is not one that seeks a universal set of moral rules or ethical standards. Instead, it is directed at moral character that is alleged to be admirable. What are admirable are virtues (e.g., civility, honesty). Further, the lack of vices (e.g., rudeness, dishonesty) is also admirable. Virtues enhance moral life. Virtues are cultivated and generally stand without question. And while virtues are not universal, they are what various cultures and societies value as good.

Virtue ethics would pivot off a central question, What kind of person should I be? Hence, how would my eventual ethical decision reflect my best character? That, of course, would depend on the promises and contracts I made with others. Moreover, how would my eventual ethical decision best avoid elements of vice? In this case, this might reflect my avoidance of self-interest or self-gain.

Social Contract Theory

Since we are all dependent on each other for our well-being, we have in effect made a contract with others we live with to understand our mutual duties as citizens. Essentially, a social contract says, I'll keep my obligations if you keep yours.

So how would contract theory apply to the addiction ethics situation presented? Again, that answer may come from asking a few simple questions. For example, if I made certain commitments to certain officials, then according to this view I have an obligation to keep my end of the bargain. Moreover, if I did not keep my end of the deal, how am I to assess and judge such an action in context of this viewpoint? What am I to do with those who don't do what they say they will do?

Feminist Theory

Recall that feminist theory does not stand on absolute rules of conduct. The focal point here is on relatedness, connectedness, and care. The key moral obligation in this perspective is to avoid harm and help people.

As applied to our example, the feminist perspective would suggest that you to drop stringent rules of ethics and morality and act from a position of care. Mostly, it would claim that whatever your final decision, it should reflect helping others and steering clear of harm. Thus, the feminist position might emphasize care for the client over rules that would entreat you to obey duty.

Ethical Egoism Theory

Egoism believes that all our ethical actions and judgments arise from a motive of self-interest. We do moral things because they make us feel good. Yet the ethical egoists would go beyond that and say we should always act in our own best interests, not in the best interests of others. This position would have you believe that you have an obligation to act in the way that best benefits yourself. Viewed in this perspective, you do not have duties to others. You have one duty and it is to yourself.

Utilizing this view for our hypothetical situation, ethical egoism would have you make your final decision based on what makes you feel the best. If excusing the client would make you feel good, then that would be the driving force for your decision. If upholding the law or your promise to the PO would make you feel good, then that would be the driving force for your ethical decision.

Relativism

If you are a relativist, recall that you essentially support the position that no one ethical view is better than another. Remember, relativism does not assume there are no ethical standards; it just states that no one ethical position is better than another. The perception of multiple sets of moral standards implies a sense of equality, which may stand as one of relativism's better points. So, in terms of our ethical example, you are stuck with the uncomfortable position of trying to figure out what is the best ethical position to use as a foundation for your decision given the circumstances described.

THE LEAST YOU NEED TO KNOW

- Practice thinking about what your final judgment would be from each perspective.
- So on what view would you base your final ethical decision?
- Most importantly, give a few good reasons for your choice.

8

How the Mind Dulls Good Ethical Decision Making

We are getting close to the chapter on critical thinking. But before we get there, we need to address another chapter that is not typically included in traditional addiction ethics books. Most ethics books don't take the time to discuss how your mind can mislead you. The signature point about this chapter is that anything that misleads can result in bad judgments and decisions, including ethical ones. The intent is to warn you that we all have a number of biases. Wright (1994) makes it a point to note while we are *potentially* moral animals, we are not *naturally* moral ones. That may help you understand many of the discussion points that follow.

Many of the biases that will be discussed in this chapter could arguably be called *mind tunnels*. These are simple, inexact, or crude rules of thumb that are favored ways of thinking. They are favored because they are comfortable and familiar, and they even assist us in getting through day-to-day activities (Taleff, 2006). The term *mind tunnels* was coined by Piattelli-Palmarini (1994) to describe favored thinking assumptions or patterns. One reason we lean on mind tunnels is that the human brain can only process so much information. So the brain automates certain thoughts or actions to reduce cognitive loads (Perkins, 2002). The point of all this is that mind tunnels—or what we are calling *biases*—have a tendency to lead us away from better addiction ethics judgments.

As with the other chapters, this one should help you identify and refine your ethical perspective.

INNATE BIASES

We will first discuss innate biases, which are unlike those built by culture or time. Innate biases were built into our brains by evolution, and they have a propensity to warp ethical decision making. To make quality ethical decisions, you need to become aware of these biases and thereafter be on guard for their constant intrusion.

At the risk of sounding dramatic, do not assume that your mind is bias free. No matter what your educational level, no matter how many workshops you have attended, or what your licenses or certificates claim, you have biases. And just when you think you're confident of your judgment, just as you feel you're right about certain ethical issues, those very feelings could well be a sign of your bias. Moreover, Wright (1994) makes the point that through evolution, your brain is, in large part, a machine for winning arguments for its owner. It has evolved to be something like a good lawyer out to defend your moral beliefs. Your brain does not want truth, it wants victory.

So to make this as blunt as possible, you and I seem to be hardwired for error (Buchanan, 2007). In addition, we have a number of other inherent biases, and those biases are sure to distort our ethical judgment. Let's examine a few of them and what we can do about them.

KNEE-JERK RESPONSES

We all do it. Those knee-jerk judgments you get after reading a newspaper headline or watching the news on TV. Some of those news items are even designed to elicit just such a response in order to keep your attention and viewership. What knee-jerk responses essentially do is bypass reasoning and jump to an assumption. All of us are vulnerable to such thinking. To press that point, here's a list of potential issues that elicit a knee-jerk response. Note how you might be inclined to skip thought in favor of a hasty response.

What is your immediate response to the following questions:

- Are today's high school teachers overpaid?
- Is there a lost generation in the United States?
- Do you have more, less, or an equal amount of free time than previous generations?
- Does texting improve one's social skills?
- Does talk therapy really work?

Now consider these questions, which have an ethical twist:

- Is it moral to tell lies to children? Even if they are about Santa Claus?
- Is it right to hire someone with less education and experience who happens to be a minority over a nonminority individual with better qualifications?
- Is it all right to tell little innocent lies now and then if they don't harm anyone?
- Should parents be allowed to withhold medical help from their children because of religious preferences?

Now consider these question, which have an addiction ethics twist:

- Should addiction counselors adopt a no-judgment stance for all clients they encounter?
- Should a family of five (including three children under the age of 6) be placed ahead of one active addict client on a housing list?
- Should an addiction counselor who slept with a client ever be allowed to re-enter the profession?

Notice that however you judged these issues, there is a certain believability that comes from a knee-jerk response versus one that comes from a reasoned critical thinking response (Riniolo, 2008). One reason is that knee-jerk responses often come with a great deal of passion, and many believe that passion trumps reason or evidence. Second, passion may appear as assurance, when compared to the milquetoast reasoned approach. As with many biases, we tend to find our conclusions first, and then add justification later (Buchanan, 2007).

For the time being, just be aware that this first instinctive way of responding to issues is ever present. We will shortly get to some ways to slow down such knee-jerk judgments.

MEANING MAKING

Not only do we have the knee-jerk biases, we have also developed a certain desire to make sense of things. Becoming aware of this natural desire will help you and your colleagues think more critically, especially when you have to make addiction ethics judgments.

We humans seem to be a belief-making (Wolpert, 2006), causality-seeking (Kida, 2006), meaning-making species. This simply means that the human brain has evolved to make sense of things. It organizes things. That means all kinds of things, be they internal or external (Wolpert, 2006). We are hard pressed to let any observation go by without attaching some kind of belief or meaning to it. If something happens in our neighborhood, or on the other side of the world, we often automatically impose some meaning to it. For example:

- Natural disasters. For example, a hurricane strikes a city along a faraway coastline, or an earthquake levels a town along a fault line, and before you know it someone is telling a TV reporter that the disaster area was devastated because it was a haven of sinners and was justifiably punished by the wrath of God (thus imposing meaning onto it).
- Death. For instance, someone down the street is unexpectedly killed in an automobile accident, and some neighbor up the street will inevitably say (impose meaning), "It was their time."
- Therapy. For example, a client leaves a long-term treatment program and within 1 week relapses. Some counselor in that program is bound to say (impose meaning) that the relapsed ex-client slipped back into denial or that "He just didn't get it yet."
- Randomness. For example, if you've ever been gambling in a casino and said something like, "I've played this slot machine for 20 minutes and it's cold." Or, "I've been watching the roulette numbers and red 9 hasn't hit for awhile. It's due." (Legitimate gaming machines and table games operate randomly; however, you are attaching meaning to the numbers that come up.)

The point here is to show how we impose meaning on things. We seem unable to let anything go by without imposing some tiny bit of meaning on people and events. And the really big point is that all those meanings come with baggage or bias.

For a fun little exercise, search your memories for any such meaning you might have made of local or worldwide events.

The way in which you make meaning of things has everything to do with what you have. What that means is that you will tend to judge people and events with your current mind-set, or in the way you understand the world (Hallinan, 2009). Another way of stating this is that you will impose meaning on events and people with what is most available or predominant in your mind. For example:

- If you tend to see the world through a religious viewpoint (it doesn't matter which one), you will impose meaning via the key principles of that religion. Generally, that will be in terms of concepts such as sin, salvation, or grace, among others. People with this predominant mind-set will do the same for moral and ethical situations.

- If you tend to see the world in terms of politics, you may begin to impose meaning on events and people in terms of traditional values, progressive values, and so forth. People with such allegiances will tend to see moral and ethical situations through the same perception set as their politics.

- If you see the world and those in it from a philosophical perspective, then you are in trouble (just kidding). However, consider the various moral viewpoints we examined in chapters 5 and 6 and how they see ethics quite differently. And all this is just the tip of the philosophical iceberg.

Stepping a little closer to addiction ethics issues, we can see that there are any number of ways to make meaning of addiction. They will entice you into making meanings out of your clients and addiction events according to their main precepts. For example:

- 12-step philosophy. Here the problem of addiction is often perceived as a character fault, mixed with the traditional disease model of addiction. If one is personally in the process of recovery, and chooses to follow this format, then one is expected to do a moral inventory, share it, and make amends to those one hurt during the active addiction. You are not seen as purposefully wanting to be an addict, but you are certainly seen as being responsible for your actions once the recovery process starts, because of the insistence on making amends.

- Social learning. In this perception, people become addicted to substances not from a disease, but from a habit gone terribly out of control. The meaning placed on clients here is one of, "You learned to become an addict, so you can unlearn it." The position does not posit a particular moral position for past improprieties. And one could argue that it goes out of its way to keep a moral neutral position. So addiction ethics issues are difficult to assess via this perspective. Social learning might even declare that its core foundation is based on science and not philosophy or certainly a position that avoids telling individuals what they should do. Social learning holds no such position on what one ought to do.
- Existentialism and person-centered ethics. These two views hold certain perspectives in common (Miller, 2005). Among other things, they place importance on self-awareness, as well as a world awareness that makes one open to more choices and therefore more responsible. Gaining this awareness is said to come from focusing on one's feelings. Both views place emphasis on the importance of the therapeutic relationship, which is authentic, empathic, and essentially human. Such relationships set a model for the client to follow and hopefully observe in other useful relationships.

The point is that whatever your religion, politics, philosophy, or view on addiction, you will see addiction ethics issues accordingly. Now this it not to say that such positions are bad or wrong. But when people, even addiction professionals, hold fast to a certain position, those very positions hold the seed of inflexibility that can crowd out other competing positions.

DIAGNOSTIC BIAS

We are overeager to label people as well. This is called *diagnostic bias* (Brafman & Brafman, 2008). We often do this labeling based on our initial observations and opinions. We cannot stay neutral for long when it comes to people. What's worse, we seem to have a difficult time re-evaluating such judgments once we make them. Consider the problems associated with ethical judgment that might present as you hear an ethical situation that arises with a colleague or with a client.

SIMPLIFICATION

Our brains have a built-in propensity to simplify things like complex problems. We did not evolve to solve complex issues; we didn't need to. Life, hundreds of thousands of years ago, was not that complex. Propagate, eat, and avoid being eaten. Yet our lives have certainly become more complex since then. The problem is that our brain development has not kept pace. So we are left with a mechanism that still wants to keep things simple.

One example of this propensity for simplification is how many of us are prone to supplying straightforward answers to complex ethical problems. One example of that is the exercise we did in chapter 1 about Willy, the counselor who had a boundary crossing with a client in which he paid her to clean his house. If you recall, you may have jumped to some early conclusions as you read the first set of variables about poor Willy's situation. But, as the story became more complicated, it might have dawned on you how the simple answers you initially supplied no longer quite fit.

Now can you imagine what some people do to complex ethical situations and dilemmas? Moreover, our brains like to jump to conclusions, see what they want to see, and hear what they want to hear (MacDonald, 2008). This brings us to the next section.

Right alongside meaning making and simplifying are the human traits of seeking patterns, beliefs, and strengthening and maintaining our beliefs (Riniolo, 2008). There happen to be three particular biases that fall under these broad conditions. We review them here because while there are benefits to be had from seeking patterns and maintaining beliefs, there are drawbacks as well. The point is for you to be aware of them so they do not cloud your ethical judgment.

CONFIRMATION BIAS

As humans, we have a tendency to look for any evidence, data, or supporting beliefs that are consistent with our beliefs. We even look for evidence to support our false beliefs. What is of particular note is that we rarely go out of our way to find information that will discredit any of our beliefs (Riniolo, 2008). This pattern—actively seeking affirmation of our beliefs and avoiding information that does not corroborate our beliefs—is called *confirmation bias* (Kida, 2006; Shermer, 2004; Vaughn, 2008). This bias is so powerful that when forced to confront evidence that does not match our beliefs, we will find a way to criticize, distort, or dismiss it (Tavris & Aronson, 2007). Now the big problem with confirmation bias is that we can end up accepting claims that are not true, finding relationships that don't exist, and finding confirming evidence that isn't genuine (Vaughn, 2008). Imagine what this kind of thinking does to those who only find confirmation for their addiction ethics judgments.

There are a number of ways to easily observe confirmation bias in action. For one, pay attention to those with strong political affiliations, and their unswerving loyalty to a certain position, or politicians who hold fast to a political stance. They seem always to find data that confirms their position. Watch certain people hang on to social stereotypes, despite evidence to the contrary of their position. They seem to find only evidence that supports and confirms their beliefs. Finally, you can see it in the way certain addiction professionals hold persistently to certain models of addiction. They often appear to process only the information that adds to their belief systems, or they associate only with those who hold the same views (Taleff, 2006).

More to our point, observe individuals who hold fast to an ethical judgment and refuse to give it up despite evidence and information that might change their initial judgment. As an illustration, consider an addiction counselor who judges a client guilty of stealing from a fellow client in an inpatient dorm. The counselor has never liked this client and feels the individual is sneaky and untrustworthy. Moreover, the evidence seems solid: the client in question was seen in the area of the stolen property and has been observed in and around other clients' bed areas. The counselor now confronts the client, and, of course, the client denies the accusation. Yet deep inside the counselor believes that client really did the crime. In this counselor's mind, there is no amount of argument or pleading from the accused, or other clients' vouching for the client's whereabouts during the robbery, that will change the counselor's belief. This perception cannot but bias future interactions with said client. That bias holds the potential for unfair future assessments and possibly unfair posttreatment recommendations. That and other such potential ethical scenarios are the result of confirmation bias.

BIASED ASSIMILATION

Now that you can spot how we tend to only gather information consistent with our beliefs, be aware that our inherent bias does not stop there. It happens with our current beliefs. With this bias, our preconceived notions hinder our ability to objectively and critically analyze evidence and data. This is called *biased assimilation* (Riniolo, 2008).

If there is one thing that really good thinking requires you and I to do, it is to impartially analyze evidence. But, with biased assimilation, our predetermined ideas contort and warp incoming information. This is where this bias does its particular damage. It influences our objectivity. Many of us seem to filter reality so as to preserve our beliefs (Buchanan, 2007).

Examples of this phenomenon include believing that data and argument contrary to a prized belief is, itself, biased and therefore should not be believed. Or holding a soft and uncritical standard as it applies to one of your prized beliefs, and then turning around and raking over the coals any contrary arguments or information leveled against your belief.

In terms of addiction ethics, consider an addiction counselor who has a long history of working with heroin clients. He has seen what he considers the worst in human behavior occur with clients who are dependent on the substance. He has heard one story after another of how people survive by doing all sorts of things to get their next fix. The constant stories have had a familiar ring. Clients become hooked and then have to come up with money to buy the next bag by doing all sorts of unethical things, then they suffer consequences, and so on and so forth.

Years later, and after listening to countless clients, the counselor finds himself again listening to a new client begin his or her story. The counselor soon jumps to the conclusion that this client is just like all the rest (a preconceived notion). The problem is that our counselor doesn't even listen closely to the new client because of the preconceived bias he has in his head. So if something new or different about a client seeps through, our counselor will dismiss the notion because of the biased preconceptions. The morality implication here pivots on the fact that his preconceived notions will influence the way the counselor will treat this new client. He will treat the new client like all the rest. That approach may in fact not work with the new client, but our counselor, with his biased assimilation, will not recognize this problem, and the client will not get the best possible treatment. Not only is this unsound treatment, but it is a truly moral and ethical problem.

BELIEF PERSEVERANCE

In light of substantial discrediting information, we tend to hold fast to a prized belief, especially one that we have gone to great efforts to construct (Riniolo, 2008). This is known as *belief perseverance*. There is nothing new or special about this bias. At its core is something most of us know: once we form a belief, we become resistant and even in some cases dead set against information that is incompatible with it. This does not mean it is impossible for us to change our beliefs. It means we are biased toward maintaining our established and cherished beliefs. Said another way, we allow conviction to trump evidence (Buchanan, 2007). Yet this preservation of belief, particularly false belief, comes at a cost, sometimes an ethical cost.

Consider the addiction counselor who holds fast to the belief that a certain treatment is the best and only treatment to offer clients—all clients. Now the clinical, if not ethical, cost is that perhaps the treatment used is not appropriate for certain clients. However, when confronted with this possibility, our counselor refuses to change. He continues to use the same treatment with every client he encounters despite outcomes that may not favor this approach. This is the belief perseverance bias in action.

Well, as if that wasn't enough, there are more inherent biases we seem to be stuck with. Kida (2006) lists a number of them. While we have covered a few already, we briefly look at those not discussed and how they can bias our ethical judgments.

STORIES VERSUS FACTS

Stories move us. They enrich our lives and give us enjoyment. We seem particularly attracted to personal stories. Moral issues often come in that form. (Hollywood has made billions on good stories.) Yet a couple of problems arise with stories. First, they are often of an anecdotal nature, and many people sadly take stories as bedrock knowledge. The big problem is that while enraptured by such stories, we ignore other relevant information that in the case of an ethical judgment could be of significant importance.

For example, a treatment program advertises itself as having a high success rate. In its advertisement, it states something to the effect that clients who come to this program leave enriched. A supposed client is shown telling how wonderful this program was and how it transformed her life. This story is meant to impress potential referral sources to send their clients to this supposedly successful program. However, if you examine the program more closely, you may find out that they only took into account those clients who had managed to accrue sizeable recovery time and conveniently did not include the many clients who relapsed following discharge. So while the story was moving, the facts were not. That has ethical implications.

MEMORY PROBLEMS

It may be disconcerting to many readers to find out that our memories are not like retrieving a computer file or replaying a tape. Memory is actually *reconstructive,* which means that each time you recall a memory, you actually modify it a bit. This makes memory prone to *confabulation,* or the replacement of facts with fantasies. Science has determined that some people even confuse an event that happened to someone else with one that happened to them (Tavris & Aronson, 2007).

If two people recall the same memory and one is different, we usually assume one person is wrong or lying. Well, it turns out the other guy may not be wrong or lying, but actually justifying what he believes his memory truly is. Memory tends to even things out and allow confirmation bias (remember that little bias?) to hum along, triggering us to forget discrepant and disconfirming information about the beliefs we hold dear. Once we have a story or a belief of ourselves or others have a story or a belief of their lives, we both tend to shape that memory to fit the story and belief. Put simply, we spin memory (Tavris & Aronson, 2007).

A process called *cognitive dissonance* drives this spin. It is a state of tension that exists whenever a person holds two psychologically inconsistent cognitions (ideas, attitudes, beliefs, opinions). A clear example is feeling caught between the idea of total abstinence and harm reduction. Cognitive dissonance comes with baggage because it produces tension. We don't rest easy until we find a way to reduce the tension. Hence, we often resort to justification, and that justification tends to distort our memory. By far the most distortions and confabulations of memory are those that serve to justify and explain our lives (Tavris & Aronson, 2007).

There are three important things to know about memory:

1. How taken aback we are to realize how a vivid memory that was full of emotion and detail is wrong.
2. That being completely certain a memory is accurate does not mean that it is.

3. How errors in memory support or justify our current feelings and beliefs.

One last little thing about *justification.* It is not quite the same as lying. A lie is a fabrication. Self-justification, while it misrepresents, also allows people to convince themselves that whatever they did was the best thing they could have done in a particular situation (Tavris & Aronson, 2007).

Now consider the potential ethical implications of relying exclusively on memory when it comes time to testify in an ethics hearing, for example, or justifying an ethical decision made by an addiction professional.

BELIEVING YOU ARE RIGHT

Have you ever had a feeling of certainty? Sometimes it can be pretty powerful. Yet, despite how good certainty feels, that feeling turns out not to be the product of a conscious choice or even a thought process. What science has found is that the state of certainty arises from involuntary brain mechanisms like other feelings. On a personal level, this general finding applies to your feelings of rightness and conviction. This very same sentiment applies to the many addiction professionals over the years who have expressed certainty through their ideas, books, workshops, and various pronouncements. Years later, we find such certainty of the time to be dated. This presents problems. Why? Simply put, even if you have a feeling of certainty that feeling may not really be accurate. This applies for your convictions of ethical standing or decision making that are achieved without reason.

Logic and reasoning are rarely convincing in the same manner as the feeling of certainty. The more one is certain of a belief, the harder it is to relinquish that belief, despite any level of contradictory evidence. The conflict between logic and a contrary feeling of knowing tends to be resolved in favor of the feeling. In turn, we often use tortured logic to justify the powerful sense of knowing what they feel we know. This is a good definition of bias (and it exists when it comes to moral decisions and judgments).

There is a deep underlying neurophysiological basis that drives the feeling that you are right, which overpowers rational thought. It is deep in our limbic brain system. A sense of knowledge comes from a different region of the brain (Burton, 2008).

There is a temporal sequence to this feeling of knowing, First, you think the thought, then assess the thought, and finally convince yourself that you are correct. This gives authority to knowing and makes it so convincing (Burton, 2008). The same can apply to moral judgments and decision making. These connections appear to happen at a subconscious level, and once judged correct they are then passed to consciousness. This subconscious element is what makes knowing so devious.

At some point during our evolution, our brains developed the ability to produce abstract thought. Because this is a relative latecomer in our development, it needed an appropriate reward system to know when it was on the right track. That reward is the feeling of knowing. Hence, the hunches, gut feelings, and beliefs of profound certainty. Say hello to abstract thought's authenticator (Burton, 2008).

The advantage to the feeling of certainty is that it avoids the important "yes, but" element. Second-guessing yourself with "yes, but" thinking is a recipe for perpetual inaction and indecision. So evolution may well have found a way to make it feel like you are right and to avoid subjecting yourself to unending self-doubt and questioning (Burton, 2008).

Notice that any thought that is less than certain and involves the lives of others has an undeniable moral component. Consider, for example, someone who is convinced she is building safe cars or buildings, creating reliable drug and alcohol treatments, and certainly making good ethical judgments on complex addiction issues.

Finally, the feeling of knowing might seem as though it occurred in response to a thought when it actually preceded a thought. For example, you may well be convinced that your therapeutic interventions over the years have been beneficial to clients, only to find out some may have actually been harmful. You may have made a decision to send a client back to prison because of your strong conviction that the client was lying at the time about breaching a treatment contract. However, months later, you find out the client was set up by a resentful partner. Feelings of knowing and certainty happen to us, and in terms of moral judgments and decisions, that "happened to us" feeling might bias us. It goes without saying that such bias will distort our addiction ethics decision making.

FALSE PRIDE

While not exactly a bias, pride or what we will refer to as *false pride* is certainly a significant contributor to bias. On the one hand, pride in a job well done is a good thing, but when it turns to vanity, the feeling can inflate an ego to the point of overestimating our abilities (Tavris & Aronson, 2007). Overestimating abilities can lead to serious bias, bad thinking, and certainly bad ethical decision making.

There are some classic false pride behaviors. Adler spelled them out many years ago, and they still hold relevance now. A short list of false pride behaviors and their effect on ethical judgment follow (Adler, 1927/1954).

- Always behaving in ways in which you are always right and others are wrong. (Consider the implications of someone using this standard as a basis for ethical decision making.)
- Belittling others in order to make yourself feel superior. (Is this a perspective one wants to use when making ethical judgments?)
- A constant and noticeable presence of hostility. (Again, is this a feeling or attitude one wants in judging addiction ethics problems?)

ANCHORING AND CONSERVATISM

We need to add two other points to all the other biases or mind tunnels already listed. The first is called *anchoring* (MacDonald, 2008). This has to do with making quick unthinking decisions, and again we have all done it. See something or someone you like, and we tend to focus on one detail (often one that stands out) and ignore the whole picture. Our brain doesn't like to mull over situations. It is built to make decisions quickly and decisively. So once a decision is made we are apt to anchor to it and tend not to fine-tune that decision. Without much effort, one can see how this might impair ethical decisions.

For example, read about a hideous crime, and more times than not, we make a quick decision as to guilt or innocence. Once this decision is made, and even if confounding evidence is found, we tend to anchor to our initial judgment. Further, consider how anchoring interferes with addiction clinical and ethical decisions. A client is accused of bringing drugs into a program, and we quickly anchor to a decision about guilt or innocence. The problem is that any confounding information presented for or against the client is thereafter often ignored. Not very clinical, and not very ethical.

Anchoring goes hand in hand with *conservatism* (MacDonald, 2008). As the word suggests, once we make a decision we tend to stick to it thick or thin. It is this stickiness that shows itself in the preceding example where people are reluctant to change their made-up minds. This holds especially true with longer-held beliefs as in the confirmation bias discussed earlier. Again, if conservatism keeps you from changing a decision—even in the face of new and contradictory evidence—then this is not clinical or ethically wise.

Wolpert (2006) ends his book (*Six Impossible Things Before Breakfast*) with the pessimistic stance that our belief systems love quick decisions (not pensive ones). We humans are bad with numbers and statistics, but we love representativeness, and we see patterns where none exist. All this gives a wonderful feeling of comfort, if not meaning, to our lives. It makes us human. That said, there is one last point to all this talk of bias. It is to press you on how confident you now can be of your ethics, now that you know something about bias and the inherent tendency of our brains to mislead us. How can you be so sure of your ethical stances?

If there is a modicum of doubt, consider using critical thinking principles to improve your ethical judgments and reduce bias, which happens to be the subject of our next few chapters.

THE LEAST YOU NEED TO KNOW

- Recent discoveries have illuminated how the human mind contains built-in mechanisms that dull thinking.
- Confirmation bias—Seek only information to confirm personal beliefs. Then actively avoid information that does not support your beliefs.
- Biased assimilation—Preconceived ideas inhibit critical analysis.
- Belief perseverance—Hold fast to a belief despite conflicting evidence.
- Cognitive dissonance—This is a state of tension that exists whenever a person holds two psychologically inconsistent cognitions (ideas, attitudes, beliefs, or opinions).
- Memory is not the accurate record of life people believe it to be.
- Justification—This misrepresents and allows people to convince themselves that whatever they did was the best thing they could have done in a particular situation.

- The sense of belief you feel when you are right may be fooling you.
- Pride—False pride can lead you to overestimate your abilities.
- Anchoring—This refers to sticking to a decision or judgment and not fine tuning it.
- Conservatism—This refers to the stickiness of a made decision.

9

The All Important Need
for Critical Thinking

We finally have come to that point where we take on the nuts and bolts of critical thinking. Many of these sections are adapted from Taleff (2006). First, we look at key principles and then jump into how all this applies to moral and ethical reasoning. For those of you who are new to critical thinking, this section will ease you into the important sections coming up. For those familiar with critical thinking, consider it a quick review.

CRITICAL THINKING PRINCIPLES AND PROCESSES

We first need to step back again and take a long look at thinking in general. Taleff (2006) made note of the need to distinguish between merely thinking and causal thinking in terms of overall addiction issues. Merely thinking is like having random thoughts run through your mind without much order or a particular link from one thought to another. This kind of thinking can be pleasant and even fun at times. However, merely thinking doesn't set out in any particular direction, nor does it end with a conclusion.

Causal thinking, on the other hand, is a sequence of thoughts that is connected with such words as "because" or "that's why." Hopefully that is what addiction professionals do when they conduct assessments on clients: They link a series of reasons together in order to assess or judge what treatment intervention would be best for a particular client. The same goes for ethical judgments. They pull together a sequence of thoughts that leads to a solid conclusion or ethical judgment. Causal thinking is mental processing that gets us closer to critical thinking.

This connection between a beginning thought and a concluding thought is called an *inference* (Baggini & Fosl, 2003). It insists that one thought be linked to another. No meandering or leisurely thinking is associated with inference. The better the link between thoughts, the stronger the inference. Obviously, the weaker the link is, the weaker the inference, and hence weaker the argument you are trying to make. How to build stronger inferences and avoid weaker ones is a focus of this chapter. We will also take a close look at what constitutes good arguments.

Another important point is that critical thinking always asks questions. Questions press at inferences and arguments in order to shake things up and discover if they are really true or not. If the shaking up process does little or no damage to the argument or inference, then it is (probably) a safe bet that the inference and arguments are good. If the questioning, however, punches holes in your argument, well, it's time to discard the inference in question and move on. When making ethical judgments, we need to get as close to the addiction ethics position as possible. So questions will show, better than most processes, not only what is indeed true but what makes it so.

ARGUMENTS

The core of critical thinking rests on the *argument,* or a set of claims that attempts to persuade (Bowell & Kemp, 2002; Thomson, 1999). It is a thoughtful procedure (Curtler, 2004). In order for a line of reasoning to be considered an argument, you need two key ingredients. You will need a claim or *conclusion,* or what could be called the product of an argument (Baggini & Fosl, 2003). That product will need to be supported by the second ingredient: reasons, or what are technically called *premises* (Hughes, 2000; Thomson, 1999). Premises supply reasons and facts, which help you to better accept, and trust a conclusion (Hughes, 2000; Moore & Parker, 1995). (See Figure 9.1.)

As an example, if an addiction program somewhere makes the claim that potential clients should come to it because it is "nationally recognized," you now have an argument. This particular argument has a principal

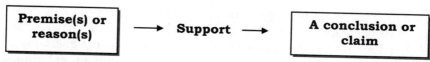

Figure 9.1 Basic argument.

conclusion (come to our program) that is supported by a premise—it is nationally recognized. However, the astute critical thinker may question why "nationally recognized" is considered a premise in the first place. What does that have to do with better treatment outcomes? It seems a better premise would be to cite outcome research: "Come to our treatment program because 90% of our clients remain sober in the first year after they leave, and we have the data to prove it." Such a premise would be a more persuasive one (if not a more ethical one) for clients to attend such a program. This is an example of critical thinking in action. It presses one to examine premises and conclusions used in the argument process. The good thinkers in our field won't stand for sloppy arguments.

One last point: do not confuse the fine art of critical thinking arguments with the loud, screaming versions sometimes seen on certain TV programs or, sadly, in some addiction programs. While critical thinking arguments can become passionate, they are not intended to reach the level of verbal insult or physical exchange.

Clarity

So far, we have only addressed the essential components of an argument. There are a few other fine details to examine. The first is called *clarity* (Moore & Parker, 1995). When you listen to an argument, the clarity of that argument demands the following:

- The argument be plainly defined
- The argument be understandable
- The argument be one where the presenter is not merely trying to win followers (which borders on the unethical)
- The argument has ample evidence for its principle conclusion
- The argument is free of ambiguous or vague statements or premises

If an argument can be construed to have more than one meaning, or if it lacks clear meaning, it is ambiguous. Ambiguity is created by not using the best words to support the argument. As Chaffee (2003) points out, clear language invites clear thinking and vice versa.

In addition, ambiguity is created by not having clear conclusions. If arguments are vague, it is because their meaning is inexact and imprecise (Moore & Parker, 1995). Examples of ambiguity in the addiction field include sweeping claims such as the claim that wide swaths of our society have some form of addiction or deny their addiction. Such claims tend to be overly widespread so as to cover an entire population without providing an explanation of how such a condition can exist. While they are meant to warn people of problems, they provide no substance for such a conclusion. They become something like your daily newspaper astrology reading, so wide open, so ambiguous that anyone can relate to it. Such wide-ranging definitions and inclusions can no longer differentiate, distinguish, or discriminate. Definitions by nature are designed to be specific and exclude people and things rather than being all-inclusive.

The addiction field, in particular, can no longer afford ambiguity and vagueness. Clarity of thought demands precision and specificity. This is especially true when it comes to making a differential diagnosis for our clients. Ambiguity is not beneficial in diagnosis. In fact, there may be ethical problems associated with such a practice. Rather, it is important to know exactly what a client's problem is. In turn, such specificity can lead us to better treatment selection. As always, it is the client who will benefit from clear thinking.

Relevance

Another fine point has to do with whether the evidence for a claim is relevant to the conclusion. This is called a *warrant* (Booth, Colomb, & Williams, 1995). For example, if someone aims to make a point about the psychological elements behind the onset of addiction, we expect psychological evidence, not moral evidence, to be in the premises. Essentially, when someone presents an addiction argument (or an addiction ethics argument), he needs to keep his facts linked to the points and conclusions of the argument.

Qualification

The last argument fine point is the *qualification* of the conclusion (Booth et al., 1995). Basically, any theory in the addiction sciences field cannot have a universal application across all clients. Theories are, by nature, limited to certain segments of a population, region, or time. For example, a particular treatment that works in one segment of our society may well not work in another. Why? For one, cultures differ, and what works in one region or culture may not work for another.

Second, there is the element of time. A treatment that was relevant in the 1960s may not be at all relevant today. There is simply no 100% certainty as to the accuracy of any one model of addiction. Times change, people change, and more scientific discoveries are sure to be made. Sooner or later, much of the information we have today will become dated. So, for the time being, addiction claims expressed by authors, faculty, counselors, or workshop leaders needs to include a range of words that suggest qualification. Some of those words include *presumably, probably, in most cases, maybe, perhaps* (Allegretti & Frederick, 1995). Critical thinkers know to keep a sharp eye on material they read and hear for its inherent restrictions, limitations, or stipulations.

ARGUMENTS AS THEY RELATE TO THE ETHICS OF ADDICTION COUNSELING

Taleff (2006) indicated that a client diagnosis, an interpretation of behavior, or the choice of a particular treatment approach you select for a client are all really just arguments. What does this have to do with ethics? One ethical problem is that repeatedly giving an incorrect diagnosis, misinterpreting behavior, or selecting inappropriate treatment approaches could be potentially costly in terms of ethical accountability and beneficence. These issues should be a signal to a counselor that he or she needs further training on how to avoid such problems. But again, what does this have to do with addiction ethics? Well, you owe it to your clients to be well-prepared and trained (accountability is an ethical principle). And if you continue to work without correcting these deficits, you might unintentionally inflict harm on a client. "Do no harm" is an ethical rule under the realm of nonmaleficence.

With these definitions in mind, a short review of a few key addiction counseling issues and their association to critical thinking is in order. This review is intended to press the issue of professional accountability or even decrease the possibility of inadvertently doing harm. All are ethical issues.

Consider the diagnosis. When you assign a diagnosis (or a cluster of diagnoses) to a client, you base it on a set of inferences, reasons, warrants, and qualifications. If done well, all these critical thinking fundamentals will lead you to a confident diagnosis or conclusion. The same applies to observing client behavior clearly without a lot of bias. This is especially true for treatment selection. Bear in mind that haphazard treatment selection can harm clients primarily because such a selection is not thought out, which means it could be wrong. That could spell unnecessary problems for the client.

Adapted from Fisher (2001), here are a set of critical thinking guidelines to refine your clinical judgment and thus reduce the possibility of assessment or treatment error and possible harm:

- Giving solid reasons for a particular diagnosis
- Basing reasons on reliable data
- Citing evidence for the selected treatment approach used in a particular case
- Citing the strength of your inference as to an interpretation
- Citing the warrants that justify your interpretations
- Allowing for any limitations to a diagnosis you make
- Allowing for limitations for an interpretation you make
- Taking into account limitations for treatment selections you make

ARGUMENT TYPES

Now it's time to examine a few types of critical thinking arguments. There are a variety of these arguments, and they extend from the simple to the complex (Hughes, 2000). We summarize a few examples.

As we saw, to be called an argument, the arrangement must have a conclusion and at least one premise. Generally, the premises (reasons) are listed first, but not all the time. The conclusion generally follows the premise and is generally just preceded by identifier words such as, "so," "therefore," or "hence." For instance, in the *simple argument* type you have one premise (P) and one conclusion (C). An example might be "As a supervisor, I note one of my counselors has over-stepped his professional boundary (has dated) with one of his clients" (P), and I conclude, "My counselor has committed an ethical violation" (C). (See Figure 9.2.)

Another type of argument is called a *complex argument*. Complex arguments often have two (or more) related premises and one conclusion (Hughes, 2000). In this case, both (or all) of the premises are needed to make a claim. One or the other premise cannot make the conclusion alone; both are needed. For example:

P1. Every addiction counselor has the ethical obligation to do no harm in therapy.

P2. Jamie is an addiction counselor.

C. Therefore, Jamie has an ethical obligation to do no harm. (See Figure 9.3.)

In another complex argument form, we again can have two or more premises, but each premise can stand alone and still add to a conclusion. Yet when combined together, they make for a stronger argument. This is called a *V argument* (Hughes, 2000; see Figure 9.4). For example:

P1. Richard knows not to do harm in therapy because it is an ethical obligation.

P2. Richard also knows not to date clients because it is an ethical boundary violation.

C. Therefore, Richard is an ethical addiction counselor.

Figure 9.2 Simple argument.

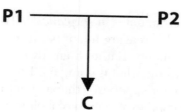

Figure 9.3 Complex argument.

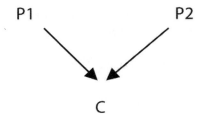

Figure 9.4 V argument.

There are other complex argument types that are variations on the basic types just shown. They generally add one premise onto another. But if you understand the three types of arguments just listed, you have a good grip on argument types.

Near Arguments

Sometimes you might find yourself encountering things that look like ethical arguments, when really they're not. These wannabe arguments are called *near arguments,* and there are two types of them: *reports of arguments* and *explanations* (Hughes, 2000). Now, reports of arguments are just what they sound like. They report that an argument was argued in a certain way. For example, "Pedro has stated time and again, and in colorful language, that he refuses to extend a client in treatment just because the client has the insurance to cover it." This particular statement is like a snapshot of a real argument. It just spells out Pedro's decision, nothing more. Notice that it is clearly a report. It doesn't detail premises or reasons. It just makes a commentary.

Commonly, people watching Pedro will turn his commentary into an argument from just what they observed. They have not put forth a real argument—only a report of an argument. They may think they are making a real argument, but such reports lack important argument components.

The second near argument is the *explanation* (Baggini & Fosl, 2003). It is often confused with a real argument because it shares a familiar vocabulary with real arguments. Rather than advance a point, however, explanations attempt to show what is going on. For example, an addiction counselor can state to her supervisor that a client is agitated and angry. While this is a pretty good explanation of a client's behavior, it does not argue for *why* the client is angry. Another example of an explanation is that of a counselor who was seen in his off-work hours having coffee with an active client. Again, this is a clear explanation and observation, but it is not an argument, especially not an ethical one. Although useful at times, explanations should not to be confused with true arguments.

Challenging Ambiguity

Sometimes it is difficult to tell when someone is making an argument. People grumble, express opinions, make observations, make accusations, tell stories, and so on (Hughes, 2000). Implicit in these opinions, accusations, and so forth is often the presumption of an argument. But if such opinions are not stated as an argument, then they are ambiguous. Ambiguity causes all kinds of problems when it comes to getting your point across. Consequently, we need to outline a short set of criteria for what stands as sound arguments, plus present a detection kit to clarify ambiguous addiction arguments. First, we examine the criteria for solid arguments.

There are three basic criteria for a good argument (Hughes, 2000).

1. The reasons or premises in the argument must be *acceptable*. That means that premises need to be true. If they are false, how can a premise provide support for a conclusion?
2. The reasons or premises must be *relevant*. This means that premises must be related, correlated, and appropriate to the conclusion. So including premises from electrical engineering or volcanism isn't relevant to addiction ethics arguments.
3. The reasons or premises must be *adequate*. This is a matter of acceptance of degree. The more adequate the premise is the more it can support a claim. Generally, premises with a philosophical and research base will provide an adequate if not solid element to a conclusion.

Now we need to offer tribute to good old Socrates and a method he developed to attain the truth and cut through ambiguity. It is a form of questioning called the *dialectic*. It is a questioning method that discards unsound arguments and retains those arguments that stand the test of scrutiny and inspection. The process is one where you basically take a position and then question that position to assess if there are any contradictions or fallacies to your position. If there are problems, you revise or build a new position, and then question it again. If it fails again, you revise until you find something that withstands the questioning (Steward & Blocker, 1982).

The next method used to challenge ambiguity comes from Sagan (1996). He fashioned a questioning yardstick based on whether you could trust educational material (e.g., whether presented in a class, workshop, or in print) as being useful or not. The yardstick was dubbed a *baloney detection kit*. The original kit has been modified with input from Allegretti and Frederick (1995). There are two parts to it. Slight modifications are made from the original (Taleff, 2006) to include ethical and moral elements.

The Bullshit Detection Kit for Everyday Issues

- Are the ideas (ethical, clinical, supervisory, administrative, books, and articles) you hear every working day clear?
- Are the ideas (ethical ones especially) you hear in supervisory sessions or in staff meetings clear?
- In such meetings, are ethical conclusions given good evidence?
- Are the clinical and ethical premises and conclusions sound and relevant?
- Could there be any qualifications that need to be made to an ethical position or claim?

The Bullshit Detection Kit for Educational Material (e.g., Classes, Workshops, and Reading)

- Is the presenter sticking to the issue or is he or she engaging in fallacy-prone thinking?
- Does the presentation have a logical sequence of thought?
- Does the presentation make a point/claim and then provide support for it?
- Can you restate the point (write it in your own words) and note the support?
- Have the prime arguments or hypotheses been tested, or, in the ethical cases, is there sound precedence?
- Is there weight given to competing ethical conclusions, and are the rival conclusions eliminated if they fail to adequately explain the ethical position?
- Does the presentation reach a conclusion?
- Are there points of summary and closure?
- Is the argument complete?
- Is the addiction material dispensed in an emotional, knee-jerk manner, or does it endeavor to appeal to the feelings of the audience with superficial and unrelated information?

- Does the material drone on about how important the subject at hand is without ever getting to the real issue?
- Does the presenter obscure the point of an argument or address it directly?

To combat ambiguity, apply these questions to your next ethical disagreement or next college class or workshop. Your answers to these questions may be detecting bullshit.

TWO TYPES OF ARGUMENTS: DEDUCTION AND INDUCTION

With the argument fundamentals and procedures in hand, it is time to address the two time-honored types of argument—deduction and induction. We highlight how these important argument types apply to addiction ethics problems.

Deduction

This argument form has been traditionally considered the ideal form of reasoning (Cannavo, 1998). It can be referred to as *theory-driven* or *top-down reasoning* (Levy, 1997), is a type of argument designed to provide certainty, and is the most rigorous argument form (Baggini & Fosl, 2003; Bandman & Bandman, 1988). We will spend a little time on this argument type because this is the form most moral and ethical arguments take. And while we certainly use data with premises to strengthen our conclusion, ethics is about statements of what is right and wrong and statements and arguments meant to convince us of a moral position. Deduction fits that need nicely.

The deductive argument structure is fairly uncomplicated and looks similar to the basic argument forms listed earlier. But those forms can include induction as well. Deduction consists of at least two premises (reasons, statements) that are trying to make a conclusion. In a valid deductive argument, if your premises are true, then your conclusion will be true (Baggini & Fosl, 2003). Here is a very simple example:

(Premise 1) The principle of nonmaleficence states that addiction counselors should do no harm in therapy.

(Premise 2) Beverly, an addiction counselor, does no harm in her therapy.

(Conclusion) Therefore, Beverly conforms to the principle of non-maleficence.

As you can see with this deduction, as long as the two premises are true, the conclusion will be true. In the vernacular of logic, if these conditions are met, the conclusion follows *necessarily* from the premises (Hurley, 1997). Deduction implies, "I expect this would happen if" (Ray, 2000). This type of reasoning allows the thinker to make assumptions from general statements and beliefs to specific conclusions (Kurland, 1995; Magee, 1998). In the preceding example, we started with a general assumption (beneficence principle) and ended up with an explicit conclusion (Beverly conforms to the principle).

If you happen to be interested, the whole premise-premise-conclusion thing is called a *syllogism* (Kurland, 1995). While the preceding example is simple, deductive reasoning can get complex in that more than two premises can be listed. Importantly, the premises need to be unambiguous to get the assured and accurate conclusion.

Sometimes you find this form of thinking occurs in staff meetings, supervisory sessions, and especially when you are trying to make a diagnosis (Bensley, 1998). One staff member will note a premise for a diagnosis in question, then another staff member will chime in with another premise. After some clarification, a conclusion or diagnosis in this case is created. The same type of reasoning occurs when attempting to establish guilt for a program rule infraction. For the most part, the conclusions drawn from this line of reasoning are fine. But there are always problems.

First, premises have to be true. If they are not, or if they are ambiguous, the conclusion will be bogus or tainted. Second, most discussions in clinical meetings are not as clear as the example presented. They are a tangle of people talking, intermixed with unrelated side issues. These issues can range from emotional displays to thinking errors. Yet these displays and reasoning errors are often assumed to be factual despite these problems. Dubious conclusions can then be created. Here is an example:

Alcoholics are always in denial.

Robert is an alcoholic.

Therefore, Robert is in denial.

The problem with this syllogism is that not all alcoholics are in denial, which was given as the basic premise (Miller & Rollnick, 1991;

Taleff, 1997). So, even though the conclusion sounds convincing, in this case the conclusion is false. If no one questions the first premise, the clinician who made this conclusion will bring an inaccurate perception and attitude to the client, who may not be in denial. Such a perception will prompt a misrepresentation of the client and subsequent clinical troubles. A possible ethical problem with this misrepresentation is that some harm could come to the client as a result of this kind of misrepresentation.

One more detail about deductions is that the conclusions pretty much say the same thing that has been stated in the premises. This has been referred to as *circular reasoning*, which doesn't do more than repeat a claim hidden in the premises. Consequently, the big limitation with deduction is that it does not give you any really new conclusions (Cannavo, 1998).

So the caveats for using deductive reasoning are to make sure your premises are accurate and to question if you have really advanced new information or are relying too heavily on this argument form. That then brings us to the next traditional form of argument.

Induction

While deductions can guarantee the truth of a conclusion, *inductive arguments* can't pledge such results. Rather, inductions give you high or low probabilities of truth (Hughes, 2000). They always have levels of doubt swirling about their conclusions (Bandman & Bandman, 1988). This process is sometimes referred to as *data-driven* or *bottom-up processing* (Levy, 1997). With inductions, we stride into the realm of scientific reasoning. That realm is where we make fresh discoveries, unlike deductive methods.

So, you ask, what does induction have to do with moral reasoning? Given some thought, one can see that research data would have a hard time establishing a moral truth. Research data can do a lot of really neat things, but they can't tell you what you should do. However, in many ethical arguments one of the premises is often of a data nature, and hence you need to become a bit familiar with induction and the scientific method.

Scientific reasoning is about classifying observed objects, classifying behaviors, providing a description of what you saw, and then offering agreeable explanations about those observations (Magee, 1998; Youngson, 1998). Said another way:

- Observe a phenomenon.
- Form a tentative explanation or theory of cause and effect.
- Test, or experiment, to rule out alternative explanations.
- Refine and retest the explanation (Bordens & Abbott, 1996).

If the inductive premise of your ethical argument essentially passes this test, then you probably have a pretty good premise. That is precisely what you want, because it will add significant support to your final conclusion, especially if it is an ethical one.

Induction probably represents nearly all the everyday type of reasoning we do. It is practical, investigative, and really advances knowledge (Cannavo, 1998). In this argument form, we ask, I wonder what would happen if I did x to y? (Ray, 2000).

Induction is the process of leading one variable into another (Honer & Hunt, 1968). We observe and collect data and then perform inductions (lead into) generalized statements that could lead to general laws, a noble goal of science (Vivian, 1968). (See Figure 9.5.)

For example (and since we are picking on denial), many addiction counselors might believe that if all the people with alcoholism they had ever known were in denial, they would be tempted to generalize that all alcoholics are in denial.

Sounds good, but the problem is that inductive arguments are less certain than deductive arguments (Cannavo, 1998). Case in point, what would happen to a counselor's denial belief if, one day, in walked a client who wasn't in denial? Hopefully, the counselor would have to reconsider her generalized denial conclusion and modify it to fit the new facts. Similar to deduction when it comes to accuracy, induction relies on evidence that is precise and correct (Vivian, 1968). And where deductive reasoning allows you to make specific conclusions from general statements, induction extends arguments from the particular to the general (Hughes, 2000; Kurland, 1995).

Finally, a generalization arrived at through induction is a conclusion. But it is usually called a *hypothesis*. Moreover, anything worth testing

Figure 9.5 Basic scientific process.

is usually called a hypothesis, and any hypothesis can be utterly false or very probably true before it is tested (Dewdney, 1997; Hospers, 1953). For example, check any old book on addiction counseling to see how many so-called truths have held up over time. A number of those truths did not did do well. Why? Because sooner or later researchers tested those truth claims to see how they held up, and if they didn't, it meant it was time to move on.

Some People Will Simply Not Change

While that was a lot of information about critical thinking, and how to do it, one minor point remains. Despite your best efforts, despite your most critical of critical thinking, it will not guarantee a change in beliefs for you or others (Woodhouse, 1994). For people who hold strong beliefs, there is often no amount of evidence, data, or facts that will make them change their minds (Wolpert, 2006). Particularly if those beliefs on a moral stand are passionately held—those hot emotions are an impenetrable barrier to change. So don't waste your time trying to change them. The emotion adds to the belief intransigence.

When we do change our beliefs, we tend to examine rationally our thoughts when the emotions are neutral or of little consequence (Gazzaniga, 2008). However, when you think people are using rational judgment, they may not be using it in a logical manner (Gazzaniga, 2008).

Here is one last point on all this arguing stuff. If you use all these strategies and still do not come to firm conclusions, consider that many issues in ethics rarely have a firm conclusion. Do not despair. Accepting a certain lack of certainty can be seen as a matter of philosophical maturity (Baggini & Fosl, 2003).

MORAL ARGUMENTS

It's time to apply all this critical thinking to addiction ethics. Recall that morals and ethics are reasoned beliefs. And whether we like it or not, when it comes to beliefs—especially addiction ethics beliefs—you need to take a stand on the moral/ethical belief or argument. Hopefully it will be a reasoned stand. And with the moral feelings we outlined earlier, it will be a balanced and reasoned stand. To get to this position, we first quickly need to look at things close up and far away.

Ethical Thin and Thick Concepts

Baggini and Fosl (2003) outline useful ideas for understanding different ethical concepts. They help put things in perspective in the upcoming discussions. The concepts are called *thin* and *thick*.

Ethics is considered *thin* if it is used in a very general and broad moralistic manner like good/bad, right/wrong. It is like looking at something far way where you can't make out many details. Applied to the realm of addiction ethics, beneficence could well be considered a thin concept. It is very broad, covers a lot of ground, and is rather general in nature. The concept is not a done deal. There still might be room to comprehend it a bit better, so it's thin.

A *thick* concept is more substantive, more meaty and detailed. Look at something close-up and you see more features. Thick concepts are generally found in your everyday addiction ethics situations. For example, should you pad the time you spent with a client to make yourself look good? Here the issue becomes thick. Here you have to spell out what is wrong with such an act. Why is it wrong and what kind of specific ethical bind do I get myself in if I do that?

Keep thin and thick in mind as we move on, particularly through the next few chapters.

Brief Overview of Moral Arguments

Like any argument, a moral one has premises and a conclusion. Its conclusion is a *moral statement*. The big difference between moral and nonmoral statements are that the moral ones assert that some action is right or wrong, just or unjust, or something or someone is good or bad (Vaughn, 2008).

Examples of moral/ethical statements can include the following:

- Breaching a client's confidentiality without his or her permission is wrong.
- It is ethically wrong to treat clients with disrespect.
- Addiction professionals have an obligation to do no harm to their clients.
- Addiction professionals have the moral obligation to give clients the best treatment possible.
- There are ethical overtones to hastily jumping to conclusions about a client's diagnosis.

Notice that in all these simple statements, you can clearly see and feel the moral tone and flavor of the statement. Plus, if you are so inclined, you might consider which ones are thin and which are thick (see Figure 9.6).

Now here is a little trick to watch for in moral arguments. At least one of the premises or reasons has to be a moral one. The other(s) doesn't have to be of a moral nature. Finally, the conclusion is a moral statement or conclusion. If you've got this then you understand moral arguments.

There's one more little trick about moral arguments. You can't have a moral statement or conclusion from a set of nonmoral premises or reasons. As the philosopher David Hume pointed out a few centuries back, you cannot infer what *should be* or *ought to be* from *what is* (Thomson, 1999; Vaughn, 2008). You can see this clearly in the deductive method that follows.

The sky is blue.

The earth is brown.

Therefore, it is wrong to disrespect addiction clients.

It just doesn't make any sense, does it? Why? The premises don't say anything about right or wrong, they just state what is. However, insert moral premises and things change. For example,

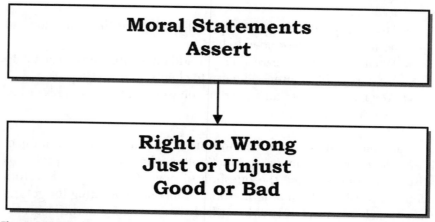

Figure 9.6 Moral statements.

It is wrong to harm addiction clients.

Disrespecting clients has a high probability of inflicting harm.

Therefore, it is wrong to disrespect addiction clients.

Notice that the first premise is a moral one. The second premise just states what is, and the conclusion is a moral statement. Certainly, one does not have to put forth as formal an example as this. Often, moral arguments can imply a moral premise and not state it. Such arguments may be of a dubious character and will require a closer examination and scrutiny (Vaughn, 2008).

Keep in mind that a moral argument, its premises, and its conclusions can be simple, complex, subtly implied, or boldly stated, just like nonmoral ones. Again, the big difference between moral and nonmoral arguments is that the moral/ethical ones argue for a moral statement (right/wrong, bad/good).

Finally, while most of us surprisingly agree on basic moral principles, it is the nonmoral premises that seem to give us the most problems (Vaughn, 2008). These premises are meant to add strength to the final conclusion, sometimes in terms of scientific evidence (Thomson, 1999). In the addiction field, such nonmoral premises are often based on a number of interesting questions:

- When choosing a treatment strategy, should empirically based evidence play a part in the selection?
- How much alcohol should a nonrecovering counselor be allowed to drink, if any?
- How up-to-date on new empirically validated therapies does an addiction counselor need to be?
- What level of self-care does an addiction professional need to have to avoid unintended harm to clients?
- At what point does an addiction counselor determine if his or her expertise has come to an end?

Take one of these questions and turn it into a premise, then inject it into the overall argument, and that's often when the ethical problems arise. For example, take the question of how "Getting too close to a client" is considered a moral question. Someone advocating for getting close to a client as an OK position will obviously argue that the closeness means that it would be OK to have coffee with a client, or have the client come over to one's apartment after a session, and so forth. That would be a premise injected in the overall argument, and it, I suspect, would be the focus of a fairly spirited debate.

A Basic Assessment Overview

At this point, we need to lay out a very broad process for assessing addiction morality/ethics issues. We then will gradually add more things to this basic approach that will allow us to really assess addiction ethics issues. So at this point, here are four basic assessment tools to use in assessing addiction ethics issues (Vaughn, 2008). (See Figure 9.7.)

- *Studying* the argument until you really understand it
- *Determining* what the conclusion is
- *Determining* what the premises or reasons are
- *Determining* the quality of the premises

OK, let's add just a little bit more to what we mean by these four assessment tools. First is studying. It means what it says—study, examine, inspect the argument. *Studying* does not mean jumping to conclusions or letting your feelings get the best of you. As noted, emotions are not bad in the assessment phase of judgment, as long as they don't overpower you. This study segment, you will note, is first on the list, because it sets up the remaining tools. Primarily by studying the passage, you want to get a good feel for an overall argument.

The next key item to establish is: What is the conclusion of the argument? As noted, this is generally easy because it will be preceded by words like "therefore," "so," "thus," or "hence." There were several arguments outlined in previous chapters, which can give you examples if you wish to review them.

Figure 9.7 Assessing moral arguments.

Next, find those premises. Recall they are the reasons that support the conclusion. Sometimes they are easy to find, sometimes not so easy. At any rate, find them and maybe even mark them with the letter *p*, or *p1*, or *p2*, and so forth. Now you are almost there.

This last part asks you to judge the quality, value, or worth of the premises. Recall that poor premises will give poor conclusions. That situation results in a poor argument, which in all probability tells you the addiction ethics argument won't fly well. A way to judge the quality is to see if the premises make sense to you. Set them against the standards of good premises outlined in this chapter. Do they feel strong or wimpy? Do they hold their own or can you see holes in the reason? You get the drift.

THE LEAST YOU NEED TO KNOW

- Inference—This is what connects beginning thoughts to a concluding thought.
- An argument—This is a set of claims that attempts to persuade, and you need two key ingredients:
  - Conclusion (claim), which is the product of an argument.
  - Premises, which are the reason(s) or fact(s) that support a conclusion.
- Clarity of an argument—This involves an evaluation of where the argument is plainly defined, understandable, and free of vague statements.
- Warrants—These are claims that are relevant to the conclusion.
- Qualification—This is the application of appropriate restrictions, limitations, or stipulations.
- A simple argument—This argument type includes one premise (P) and one conclusion (C).
- A complex argument—This argument type has two (or more) related premises and one conclusion.
- A V argument—This is a complex argument, where each premise can stand alone and still add to a conclusion, but when combined together, they make for a stronger argument.
- Reports of arguments—This refers to a wannabe argument that merely describes a commentary.
- Explanations—These do not advance a point; they merely illustrate what is going on.
- Acceptable premises—This refers to premises that are true.

- Relevant premises—This refers to premises that are related, correlated, and appropriate to the conclusion.
- Adequate premises—This refers to the degree of acceptance for a premise. The more adequate the premise, the more it can support to a claim.
- Dialectic—This is a questioning method that discards unsound arguments and retains arguments that stand the test of scrutiny and inspection.
- Deduction—This is an argument form considered to be the ideal form of reasoning, often referred to as theory-driven or top-down reasoning; it is a type of argument designed to provide certainty and is the most rigorous argument form.
- Syllogism—This is the deductive premise-premise-conclusion format of argument.
- Induction—This is an argument form that gives probabilities of truths, leaves levels of doubt about its conclusions, and is a process sometimes referred to as data-driven or bottom-up processing.
- Hypothesis—This is a generalization arrived at through induction and is a conclusion.
- Moral statement—This is an assertion about whether some action is right or wrong, just or unjust, or whether something or someone is good or bad.

10 | Ethical Fallacies

It is time for *fallacies,* those pesky processes that distort the core of good thinking and good decision making. They are mistakes, faults, omissions, and false beliefs that do everything wrong in order to make good arguments bad (Taleff, 2006). They do the same thing for ethics and, in our case, addiction ethics. While there are scores of fallacies, the more problematic ones are reviewed here. The review will be followed by a few suggestions for how to avoid becoming ensnared in these traps. The principal mission of this chapter is for the reader to recognize and assess what gets in the way of your best ethical judgments.

APPEAL TO THE PEOPLE OR MASSES (AD POPULUM)

Ever hear someone say after he has done something mildly unethical, "What's wrong with that? Everyone does it" (Curtler, 2004)? If you have, then you have been on the receiving end of those who tried to slide the old *ad populum* fallacy by you. You may have heard the phrase "everyone does it" in the context of someone on your staff trying to justify billing an insurance company for a little more than what a service actually consisted of. Or in terms of staff members taking sick time when they are not actually sick. Challenge someone who does this, and often the excuse is, "Everyone does it."

There are a few problems with this appeal (Curtler, 2004). First, everyone does it relies on another fallacy. It is called a *generalization,* and these types of fallacies often make rash judgments without much data to back them up. For example, how does one know that everyone does it? Was a survey taken? Did the survey reveal that everyone in your program and around the country indeed does charge extra time for treatment services? And even if they did, what relevance does it have on the ethical tone of the act? By asking such questions, you can hopefully start to see how weak this appeal is. To sniff out this weakness, tune your ear to the words "every," "all," or "everyone." These and other such generalizations or exaggerations are sure to tip you off that the person using those words is trying to use the ad populum fallacy.

The generalization weakness is not the most pronounced element of the ad populum fallacy. The more relevant problem is that the masses might be wrong (Curtler, 2004). So appealing to them might in turn be wrong. Why? Well, we have seen the masses be wrong over the centuries on any number of ethical issues. Think of slavery or not giving women the vote as two examples. Granted we would like to believe that in this day and age we, the masses, use a better moral framework than those from the past, but recall that ethics evolves. So you have to ask, do you really want to trust the masses as a reliable guide for your moral compass? Other elements might serve in a more reliable way.

Finally, to drive the nail in the coffin of this appeal, a significant problem with "everyone does it" is that this conclusion only allows you one of a host of ethical options. Now that smacks of narrow-mindedness in a negative, limit-producing manner, and this type of narrow-mindedness cannot by its very nature be very ethical. The simple advice here is to pause and ponder the relevance of a blind adherence to a mass of people.

BELONGING TO A GROUP

Very close to the appeal to the masses is the *appeal to the many fallacy.* One would think that if faced with an ethical problem, many heads could address the problem much better than one. While there are good arguments for this rationale, it is not always true. Many heads can enlighten and come up with creative alternatives. However, groups of people can also shield you from ethical struggles and help you avoid ethical responsibility. That is, they can be close-minded, and shield out creative or better judgments.

The process that sometimes encourages close-mindedness is called *groupthink* (Janis, 1983). Janis found that groups (even clinical groups) often suffered from this malady. They would ignore important facts, hold stereotypical views of outsiders, and silence dissent. Consider what such processes will do to the need for enlightened ethical discussion.

Adapted from Taleff (2006) are some ways to defend against this fallacy. First is the need to be cautious of the prevailing ethical view of a group. If you are in such a group, watch to see if other ethical views are tolerated or discounted outright. And be particularly attentive to stereotypical responses to ethical problems.

RED HERRING

In this fallacy, the point is to distract you from the real issues at hand. Why would someone try to do this to you? Well, for one, they might not want to address the real issue. And there could be any number of reasons for doing that. For instance, say an administrator makes a clinical decision to discharge a client early from a residential program, but the real reason for the discharge lies in the fact that the client's insurance has run out. So it is no longer profitable to keep the nonpaying client in treatment when his bed could be used for a paying customer. When confronted with what seems to be an unethical thing to do to the client in question, the administrator shifts the direction away from the client's ability to pay for bed space by accusing you of impugning his character.

As another example, consider that an administrator is caught putting program money into his pocket, and when confronted with the fact, he responds that to report him would be a mark of disloyalty. In both cases, the response is clearly not addressing the issue at hand, but rather diverting the argument onto something else that has little or no relevancy to the real issue.

The *ad populum fallacy* (Curtler, 2004) discussed earlier can also be used as a red herring. How? Well, how about a colleague who pads her client service time with a longer segment of therapy than actually occurred? When you complain that such a practice is unethical, her response is "What's wrong with that? Everyone does it." Then you have been hit with not only an ad populum, but a red herring as well. Why?

Because she has not directly answered your complaint, but has taken you in a completely different direction, as red herrings do. Another tactic is to answer you with "What! Are you some kind of a company man?" A red herring at play again. Sometimes red herrings do that. They put you on the defensive, which is often their intention.

TWO WRONGS FALLACY

A close cousin to the red herring that is also intended to lead you off track is the *two wrongs fallacy.* If used well, it can not only distract you from what is a real ethical issue but also put you on the defensive. The central ploy is to accuse you of an ethical blunder (e.g., you did it too). But the problem with accusing one of doing the same mistake is that two wrongs don't make it right (Taleff, 2006). For example, take the case of a boundary violation:

Yes, I may have seen my client a few times at the corner coffee shop, and yeah, we may have hugged after our sessions, but (to a supervisor) were you not caught doing something similar about 15 years ago?

So how can you accuse me of an unethical act, when you did the same thing?

What's the best strategy to address this kind of fallacy? One, while it can be intimidating, maintain your ground if confronted by this fallacy. Two, stand firm on the critical thinking notion that all kinds of wrong do not make anything right.

THE STRAW PERSON

This used to be called a *straw man* or sometimes a *straw woman.* Its mischievous power lies in its ability to mischaracterize an argument, or falsify a position and then pounce on the false position, making it sound like it was the original position all along (Pope & Vasquez, 2007; Taleff, 2006). Essentially, it is a silly caricature of your position, not really your position at all (Baggini & Fosl, 2003). The straw person fallacy tries to make you believe you know what the other guy is thinking or what they really mean. Yet no one has such power, but the straw person misleads into the false conclusion that the accuser indeed does know, and so should you.

One pertinent example of this pernicious fallacy would be something like a person attacking you for questioning their ethical judgment on an addiction case, and rather than strengthening their position or pointing out the flaws of your assessment, he would then accuse you (or rather, the straw person) of trying to impose draconian elements on the debate, making you look rigid. A clear mischaracterization.

CHARACTER ASSASSINATION

Should you one day find yourself losing an argument with someone, and you have no other claims or premise handy, go for the throat and discredit your opponent. That's right, rake him over the coals and call into question his character or anything else you can do to discredit your opponent. The point is that if you can dishonor the person, *ad hominem,* the fallacious thinking is that you can in turn discredit the argument (Pope & Vasquez, 2007; Taleff, 2006). It goes something like this: "My supervisor wants me to re-examine my ethics of what I told my group about how they handle their morals. But my supervisor is the last person who should be telling me to re-examine my ethics. He's a sleaze-bag. He's the one rumored to have had an affair with a client last year. This guy has some nerve, telling me to think about ethics when he is so self-righteous. Who in their right mind would take advice from him?" You get the picture. Simply be on guard for this fallacy and avoid it at all costs. If you think about it, character assassination has all the earmarks of being unethical.

APPEALS TO AUTHORITY

Recall way back at the beginning of the book there was an entreaty for you to think through the many addiction ethics issues you will face. Well, what was partly behind that plea was the *appeal to authority.* It encourages you to rely on the authority alone, not the data, or critical thought behind an appeal. You need to watch out for this fallacy, especially if the person spouting the moral appeal is not really a reputable ethical authority or if the so-called authority has a reason to mislead you (Epstein & Kernberger, 2006). For example, a marketing supervisor (kind of an authority) in your program states something to the effect that, "I don't think it's bad if you have a client wash your car after group." "After all," goes the fractured logic, "it would give that client structured time, and teach him discipline."

Encouraging clients to do your personal jobs or errands is simply wrong no matter who says it's OK. This kind of behavior crosses professional boundaries. It is all the more unethical if the person who espouses such behavior is an authority but not one with special ethical training and background.

In a larger context, many authorities have arisen in our field over the years. They have written many books, have well-manicured Web pages, and give wonderful lectures. The problem you need to watch for with certain authorities is whether they have the data and well-founded arguments to back their claims (Taleff, 2006). This is especially true in terms of addiction ethics. A characteristic to watch for is if the authority, aka guru, does not wish to debate or provide well-rounded insights for his established truths. He often pronounces some truth but smiles smugly if questioned, as if such inquiries are somehow below his consideration. Much of this kind of thing happened in the 1960s in communes around the country. The morality of the commune or camp was left in the hands of such people and, sadly, many people got hurt. In some extreme cases such authority figures ran drug and alcohol programs, and morality was left in their hands as well. Please be careful of them. Always feel free to question an expert's opinion. Solid expert opinion should stand on evidence offered by the expert and not just the word of the expert alone (Riniolo, 2008).

One last caution for authority comes from Pope and Vasquez (2007). It is the warning of using ethical codes as the final authority for ethical judgments and decisions. While very important, codes are not a substitute for deliberation or a creative response to ethical problems in your program or in your career. The fallacy of authority here is one of a thoughtless response to an ethical problem with, "Well it's a violation of our code, and we should act accordingly." The codes, to be sure, will prohibit certain actions and situations, but they cannot tell you how to judge a unique client or addiction counselor facing a unique problem. You may have to think.

A few smart strategies to offset authority type fallacies include the following (Taleff, 2006):

- Don't just take ethical positions given by authority figures at face value.
- Always look for evidence especially in the premise that an authority might invoke.
- If need be, ask the authority to clarify his or her ethical position.
- Be aware if an authority has a vested interest in an ethical position.

MISTAKING PEOPLE OR GROUPS WITH CLAIMS

While it is good to on guard for authority fallacies, one has to be aware of the fallacies of *mistaking a person or group with a claim or argument* (Epstein & Kernberger, 2006). This is similar to the appeal to authority fallacy but in the opposite direction of sorts. This fallacy deals with someone giving a very good ethical claim even if the person saying it is less than reputable. Simply put, it just isn't right to say that a claim is false just because of who said it. Think again about the previous example, in which your supervisor tells you that crossing boundaries is wrong. This fallacy would have you discount his claim because of what he has done (crossed a boundary himself). The same can be said of a group (for example, members of a particular political party) with a less than stellar ethical past, that all of a sudden turns around and petitions for a very good ethical stance.

While this particular fallacy seems to fly in the face of the appeal to authority, the real issue here is about the reputable claim and not about the less than reputable people making the ethical claims. Conversely, you can uncritically accept a false claim from a reputable person or group. If this sounds a bit confusing, such is the nature of complex addiction ethics. And you and I must grapple with such things, hence the press for critical thinking.

THE FALSE DILEMMA APPEAL

Another fallacy that drove the creation of this book was and is the *appeal to a false dilemma*. In this case, an appeal is being made to simplify something that may have many possibilities (Epstein & Kernberger, 2006). For example, someone might state, "In order to really be ethical, either you must never judge a client's past addictive behavior or you must judge that behavior with resolute standards such as the Bible or the Koran. There is no other way to be ethical." While this example is a bit far-fetched, this false dilemma illustrates the point that offering only simple alternatives does not allow for other options or possibilities, which obviously could exist. Note that those who use the false dilemma in ethical arguments may be trying to corner you into unreasonable thinking for their own agenda.

THE BELIEVABILITY OF BOLD STATEMENTS

Next is the *believability of bold statements fallacy*. Here, clients, counselors, and administrators might use strong emotional words and rhetoric to persuade themselves and others of some moral judgment or decision. The problem is that bold words are not in and of themselves evidence.

As an illustration, consider the boundary crossing counselor we have used in past examples arguing loudly and with conviction that his many professional boundary incursions were innocent and were not meant to do harm. He uses sympathy-eliciting words in an animated style, all intended to show that he is innocent and meant no harm by his actions. But his bold words are his only defense, and he uses no other forms of argument. Bold words alone, no matter how seemingly confirming, are not good reasons and do not lead to good conclusions.

IF IT STANDS OUT, IT HAS TO BE THE REASON

This is a small, but powerful, fallacy often seen when we make our first ethical judgment on a particularly striking ethical behavior. Our impulse is to pass judgment (sometimes pretty strong) on what we perceive as what stood out. Say, for example, that you watch a newscast that shows a pedestrian (make it a little old lady) mugged by a thug while others are shown standing around just watching. The newscaster spouts how people did nothing while the lady was robbed. We are apt to cast the bystanders as thoughtless, insensitive, and uncaring. It just stands out.

However, what if we discover later that another thug was just off camera yelling and swearing at his partner to hurry up and was waving a handgun at the crowd all the while? What might be your ethical judgment of the bystanders now?

While it may prove difficult, the critical thinking point to the *it stands out fallacy* is to reserve ethical judgment until you have more facts.

OVERCONFIDENCE

While at first glance, this might not appear to be a fallacy, it is listed as one of manner and style (Taleff, 2006). Such fallacies use behavior— your behavior—to do their distortion. If something can deceive using manner and style, it can be a fallacy. How? All it takes to distort or bias a judgment is overconfidence or cockiness. Most people who display this manner are not going to take the time to critically think through an ethical problem (Taleff, 2006). They are too busy being too cocky that they made the right ethical judgment already. That can lead to ethical misjudging and bias where clarity is needed.

Recommendations to neutralize overconfidence include the following:

- Hold your horses on first ethical judgments.
- Pause and see if you can build reasonable arguments that are not compatible with that first cocky judgment.
- If you really want to test how self-assured you are on your ethical judgments, write them down. Then, following the inclusion of more reasons and facts to an ethical case, check to see how accurate you really are (adapted from Taleff, 2006).

APPEAL TO IGNORANCE

The use of this fallacy may be the most illogical of all. It tries to make you believe that since there is no evidence that something is false, it must be true (Hughes, 2000; Taleff, 2006). First, let's see how this is often applied, then how it is employed in addiction ethics. Often the application is something like this:

Since no one can disprove this mark on my big toe did not come from aliens, it must have.

To press the point, none of the following statements can be disproven, but folks use this lack of truth for believing. For example:

- *Every president since Kennedy has been planted by the Lithuanians.*
- *The world will end this coming Tuesday at 3:10 P.M.*
- *There are invisible creatures from Middle Earth living in my bathroom.*

Those may sound silly, to be sure, but some people reason this way, they appeal to the lack of evidence as belief. The same can occur in addiction ethics. For example:

For the last ten years that our recovery program has been offering our brand of therapy that includes belly-button meditation, coupled with sand castle building, no one has proved that these methods are worthless or that we are unethical for providing these unique forms of recovery. That makes it clear they are meaningful, and we therefore are ethical for offering them when no one else would offer such treatments for those who need them.

No matter how interesting some of these statements may sound, resist the temptation to buy into such claims. The response to such claims is, "Where's your proof?" (Not "Where is your lack of proof?").

BEGGING THE QUESTION

Something similar to the twisted logic of appeal to ignorance is *begging the question*. Recall that arguments are supposed to have their premises support a conclusion. Not so with begging the question; here certainty or the conclusion is presupposed in its premises already. Essentially, the premises (reasons) turn out to be the conclusion (Taleff, 2006). We sometimes resort to this when we wish to defend a strongly held conviction (Hughes, 2000). And where do we often find strong convictions? You guessed it—in ethics. For example:

> *The Bible/Koran says it is the law of God, and the law of God must be true, therefore the Bible/Koran is the law.*

Some psychological examples adapted from Pope and Vasquez (2007) include the following:

> *Has your treatment program stopped using those unethical practices yet?* The question assumes a yes or no response to what is stated in the question itself (that the treatment program has been using unethical practices).
>
> *Why must you assume an uneducated strategy when dealing with addiction ethics problems?* Again, the question assumes in the question that there are uneducated strategies to begin with.

As with the appeal to ignorance, when you hear this kind of fallacy, simply ask for clarified reasons.

This list was not intended to be an exhaustive list of ethical fallacies. It just touched the surface of what pitfalls and dangers can be used to justify poor ethical arguments. The point was to introduce the reader to some of these mistakes, omissions, false beliefs, and faults.

THE LEAST YOU NEED TO KNOW

- Fallacies are mistakes, omissions, faults, and false beliefs.
- Fallacies come in a spectrum of styles from personal attacks to purposeful attempts to lead you away from the core of an argument.
- They lurk everywhere, hence you need to be alert to their forms, styles, and kinds.

11 Ethical Thinking: A Set of Procedures

We have covered a lot of material. At this point, it is time to bring together all the ideas that make possible the resolution of ethical dilemmas. One important point will be the introduction of the *ethics judgment kit*. This is a process often used in my workshops. It asks the reader to weigh the various emotions, virtues, moral positions, and critical thoughts into a process whereby one can come to reasonable and well-thought-out decisions. It also combines some of the thinking of others (Kidder, 2003). An important point to keep in mind when doing your ethical thinking is not to accept moral judgments at face value. Think of this process as a kind of legal proceeding where nothing is to be accepted without pretty good evidence and pretty good arguments (Ingram & Parks, 2002).

While there are a variety of ways to resolve ethical issues, it is time to present a general plan to address all those pesky addiction ethics dilemmas you will encounter.

THE SPIRIT OF DECISION MAKING

Before we start this discussion, we need to establish the spirit of making addiction ethics decisions. That spirit sits on a number of concepts.

One is *moral humility,* or knowing the limits of your moral understanding. Another is that humility in decision making lacks boastfulness and pretentiousness. The last is *moral integrity,* or holding oneself to the same set of rigorous standards as one would an opponent (Paul, 1993).

One last concept included in this broad framework is called *open-mindedness.* It is to be viewed as a virtue, if not an ideal. Yet there is some confusion as to what constitutes this virtue. Hare (2009) established several principles of open-mindedness. The essence of the principles is as follows:

- Open-mindedness requires consideration of alternative views, unless there is good reason to believe alternative views have no merit.
- Over-simplified versions of open-mindedness simply assume it means a ready acceptance of new ideas. This fails to account for critical examination of such ideas. Without it, open-mindedness would be chaotic and lead us into gullibility. Yet many people interpret scrutiny as a sign of closed-mindedness. Not so. Open-mindedness tries to reconcile and balance critical assessment with receptivity.
- Open-mindedness requires a sincere dedication to the pursuit of truth. This includes a concern for sound judgment, good evidence, and a readiness to change your mind.
- Open-mindedness is a desirable attitude given the limits of what we know (knowledge) and our propensity to believe errors of judgment.
- Open-mindedness requires we dispense with dogma, especially our own, and make a commitment to reflection.
- Open-mindedness asks us to include more in our judgments and decisions than our own subjective rationality. As we have seen, much of that is often distorted. Essentially, to be open-minded you cannot rely solely on what you think to be true.
- Open-mindedness needs the consideration of the best evidence possible and best thinking possible. Sometimes that means turning to the experts, books, journal articles, or personal contacts for a little help.
- Open-mindedness does not see every alternative possibility as a threat to an established ethical view. All possibilities are not equally likely.

- Open-mindedness requires tolerance, free expression, open discussion, and debate. Open-mindedness holds the promise that
  progress on intractable problems will be made one day.
- To flourish, open-mindedness needs education, the appreciation
  of intellectual virtue, and the avoidance of indoctrination.

OK, with that spirit established, we can move on.

THE ADDICTION ETHICS JUDGMENT KIT

The addiction ethics judgment kit is a hybrid of decision-making ideas
presented in Guy (1990), Thomson (1999), Curtler (2004), Ford (2006),
Taleff (2006), and Pope and Vasquez (2007). Reviewing these guidelines,
and a number of others, it became apparent that there was no simple
procedure for making ethical decisions. They were all rather extensive
because of the ever-increasing complexity of ethical problems in human
services. Essentially, complex ethical problems need complex processes
to provide direction for reasonable decisions. There doesn't seem to be
any way around that.

Besides open-mindedness, the kit is based on a few other broad
principles (Curtler, 2004). They consist of the following:

- Respect for the person
- Fairness to others
- Adopting rules that increase the happiness for the majority

One thing needs to be remembered in evaluating ethical dilemmas: It is impossible to establish an ethical principle or rule that ignores
human rights and the harm done to others (Thomson, 1999). Hence,
the hybrid kit presented here has a number of steps that we will now
examine.

1. Collect yourself and settle down.
   a. Often addiction ethics issues are cause for strong feelings.
      Blood is pumping, and faces are flush with emotion. The prob-
      lem is we don't think well at these times.
   b. Therefore, one needs to take a few deep breaths and create
      some emotional distance from the strong emotions.
   c. Consider using moral emotions to help with the process.

2. Identify the ethical problem or dilemma.

   a. Ask yourself if this is an ethical problem. (One way to figure that out is to ask whether the situation stinks. Should something be done?)
   b. Is there something wrong, an injustice done, right violated, or someone harmed?

3. Start gathering your facts and evidence. (This requires a few questions.)

   a. What do you know?
   b. Are there things you need to know, but don't?
   c. Who exactly is involved?
   d. How reliable are your facts?

4. Consult with relevant guidelines, codes, or authorities.

   a. What do your national and state ethical guiding principles/codes/standards have to say about the situation?
   b. Do you have access to reliable ethical experts if you need them?

5. Look at the identified problem through various ethical perspectives.

   a. What would this situation look like through the eyes of duty ethics?
   b. Through the eyes of utilitarianism?
   c. Through the eyes of divine command?
   d. Through the eyes of feminism?
   e. Through the eyes of other perspectives discussed earlier in this book?

6. Look at the identified problem through the eyes of critical thinking principles.

   a. If you could form an argument of the situation what would be your premises and conclusions?
   b. Are there mind-dulling processes at work here or fallacies involved in any way?

7. Now weigh the arguments and evidence and make a first probable course of judgment and action.

   a. OK, by now you have just about everything you need to make a judgment—so, what is it?

    b. How would that judgment direct a course of action, and what would it look like, keeping in mind how it would affect all the identified people involved?

  8. Rest and reflect. (Take a day off and then come back.)

  9. Now retest your first judgment and first course of action by going through steps 2–7. If your initial judgment and action held up, you may have your position and solution in hand. If not, refine till you obtain the solid solution that is needed.

10. Last item—Was this the best thing to do? If you assess that it is, then it is time to convert the judgment/decision to action.

The streamlined version is as follows:

  1. Settle down, use your emotions.
  2. Identify the ethical problem/dilemma.
  3. Gather facts and evidence.
  4. Check with guidelines, codes, or authorities.
  5. What do the diverse ethical perspectives say?
  6. What does critical thinking have to say?
  7. Assess your arguments and evidence, then make first judgment and action.
  8. Rest and reflect.
  9. Do steps 1–7 one more time.
10. If your assessment reveals that your first judgment/decision was the best thing to do, then it's time for action.

CASE STUDY

Here is an example of how this 10-step process might look in action.

    The situation: A close friend of a client calls a treatment program and urgently needs to talk to the client's addiction counselor. The close friend stopped off to see the client and has important news that has to be shared with the counselor. The friend is crying, close to hysterics, and obviously in high stress. Knowing the friend does not have a release of information signed allowing the counselor to legitimately talk to this individual, the counselor takes the call anyway. The counselor's thinking at the time is, "My client is in trouble. Besides, I can't refuse to talk to this person because she's so upset. That wouldn't be right."

The friend states that she knows her friend is a client at the counselor's center. She has information that the friend has relapsed and is threatening to hurt not only himself but also his family (mother, father, and another sibling) where the client now lives. The friend states she and the family are frightened and felt she just had to call the counselor. The counselor then rushes over to the client's residence and talks the client into going to the local hospital emergency department for an evaluation. The client becomes further agitated at the emergency room. And this action looks like it may well have averted serious violence.

From this brief scenario, it is clear the counselor breached the confidentiality of the client. After the situation settles down, the counselor marches into her supervisor's office and openly states what just happened. Now the supervisor has to make an ethical judgment call.

Using the *addiction judgment ethics kit,* how might the supervisor make the best ethical call?

1. If this situation had rattled the supervisor, he or she would have to settle his or her nerves. That might mean going for a brisk walk, taking a few deep breaths, or some other action to finally feel even tempered and get ready to do some serious thinking. Along with this, the supervisor should attempt to zero in on what particular emotion was revved up (e.g., anger, fear). Finally, the supervisor would not wish to eliminate all emotions. The particular emotion(s) elicited by the scenario might prove useful in the following deliberations.

2. In a settled frame of mind, the supervisor now needs to clearly identify the ethical problem. The clear problem is that the counselor breached the confidentiality of a client without the client's consent. The counselor disclosed the breach herself and openly admits the ethical problem. However, while the counselor admits the breach, she also noted she did it for good reasons. Her client was in trouble and she says that "I could not refuse to talk with the friend given the client's state of mind. I felt it would have been wrong to say 'I can't talk to you,' or 'just call 911.' At the same time, I took a risk in that the call could have been bogus."

3. At this point, the supervisor has to collect all the facts or evidence in order to come to a fair judgment. The facts in this case seem to be clear.

   a. First, the counselor disclosed to a stranger over the phone without written release that she indeed was the counselor of said client.

   b. The counselor readily admits to the charge.

   c. However, while the counselor breached confidentiality, obtaining the information afforded the opportunity for the counselor to acquire vital information about her client's mental status, which resulted in getting the client to a safe environment (hospital) and avoiding possible complications.

   d. Certainly, this could also have been accomplished by encouraging the friend to call 911.

4. At this point, it's time for the supervisor to consult the rule books and codes. The supervisor re-reads the state and federal standards about unauthorized disclosure. He or she states that staff shall not release information without the client's written permission.

5. Now it is time to look at this from different ethical perspectives. The supervisor looks through two opposing views: utilitarianism and deontology. The utilitarian says that the best thing to do is what will make most people happy or content. Clearly a bad situation did not turn worse by the actions of the counselor taking the call, and a lot of people (family) are happy about it. However, the duty of the counselor was to abide by the code of confidentiality, which the counselor in question did not do. The supervisor opts for judging this situation through the utilitarian perspective in that the client received the necessary help he needed, and the family was happy in return. Here the judgment was assessed as outcome over duty.

6. It's critical thinking time. Here the supervisor needs to assess how well the argument is proceeding. Is it sound? Has the supervisor used fallacies? Reviewing the situation, the argument roughly is as follows:

   a. The counselor did in fact breech a confidentiality statute.

   b. But, in the end, the best interests of the client and the client's family were served, and the client is now stable.

   c. Therefore, the supervisor concludes that the client's general welfare is the top priority.

   d. No fallacies seem to have been used to arrive at this conclusion.

   e. No apparent sloppy thinking or favoritism appears to have been in play.

7. Now the supervisor is in the position to weigh all the arguments and evidence and to make a first judgment. Reviewing things, the supervisor thinks:

   a. The evidence says that the counselor definitely did breach confidentiality (rule book), and the counselor admits to this breach. But the evidence indicates that by breaching confidentiality, a potentially dangerous situation was avoided.
   b. Reviewing general ethical theories for guidance, the supervisor elects to stay with the utilitarian approach.
   c. Critical thinking indicated a good argument was used, and there was no evidence of fallacies in use.
   d. All of this points to a first judgment of, "I will note this infraction in the counselor's personal file but not take retribution action."

8. The supervisor did a lot of work; now it's time to take some brief time off and rest. The point of resting is to put things on the back burner to simmer. After resting a day or two, the supervisor returns to the situation.
9. Now the supervisor will retest, and that means it is time to take 10 minutes and review what the supervisor did in steps 1–7. The supervisor assesses that the first round of thinking is sound.
10. Therefore, the best thing to do in this case is go with the first judgment.

Now that we have established this, what are we to do about reviewing other ethical positions?

CRITICISM OF ETHICAL ARGUMENTS

There will be a time, I can assure you, that you will want to criticize or attack (only in the critical thinking sense) an addiction ethics position. Such a position will come from the mouth of a colleague, authority figure, or in print. In keeping with all that has just been discussed, there are two prime positions from which to launch your criticism (Baggini & Fosl, 2003).

■ Criticize the truth of a premise. However, first make sure you have established what the premise is in the first place. (There is no reason to go off half-cocked by criticizing a straw person or criticizing the person and not the argument. Such attacks will only make you look foolish.)

■ Try to show that the argument is invalid, regardless of whether the premises are true or not. What you are going after here is the soundness of the ethical position you are taking to task. Essentially, one can have good premises but reason so poorly that the conclusion turns out flawed. If you see such thing, then use it as your criticism.

THE LEAST YOU NEED TO KNOW

■ Now it is time for the reader to go back and re-examine previous ethical stands they've made.

■ However, you are now to apply the steps of addiction ethics judgment kit to your previous judgments.

■ The goal is to compare the previous ethical decisions to those made with the kit.

12 Addiction Ethics Principles with a Critical Thinking Twist

No book on addiction ethics would be complete without a review of the basic ethics principles that all addiction professionals should know. The following list covers the gamut of principles that should (note the word *should*) guide our day-to-day professional if not personal conduct.

But before we get into the principles, we need to set the tone by presenting just a word about integrity and two other points. As to *integrity,* Johnson and Ridley (2008) note that it is the cornerstone of all ethics. You will see it blended within many of the upcoming principles. Essentially, integrity refers to your adherence to the ethical principles. It encompasses honesty, honor, and reliability. Integrity generally shows itself in times of adversity and the testing of your principles.

The two other points are of keeping yourself transparent and accountable (Johnson & Ridley, 2008). *Transparent* essentially means keeping your actions aboveboard, honoring commitments, and keeping your professional relationships clear. Once you begin to delve into the murky waters of evasiveness, or resort to secrecy, your credibility becomes compromised and opaque, the opposite of transparent. *Accountability* could be succinctly defined as taking responsibility for your actions, as in taking deserved blame and deserved credit for those actions. It is a high standard and includes integrity and transparency.

Depending on what you read, there are about 10 or more of these key principles (see "The Least You Need to Know" at the end of this chapter). The core list is adapted from Geppert and Roberts (2008), ICRC (1994, 1999), NAADAC (1994), Vaughn (2008), and White (2005).

For addiction counselors who have yet to take their national certification examination, it is probably a good idea to memorize these points. You are sure to see them again. For the seasoned addiction counselors, it is probably a good idea to review these points, for they are the centerpiece of solid addiction counseling ethics. You will need them your entire career.

We first list the principles in a traditional approach and then apply a little critical thinking to the mix, which adds a progressive style.

RIGHTS

This term is used in several of the ensuing principles. The concept of rights forms the foundation of many ethical problems. So we should outline a brief discussion of what exactly a *right* is (Solomon, 1993). First, a right is a demand of sorts or a claim, not unlike an argument conclusion. Rights have obligations that guaranteed right to freedom of speech. Rights can emanate from one person to entire societies.

Rights come in different flavors (Solomon, 1993):

- *Legal rights* are those rights guaranteed by law or constitutions. Laws make these rights, and they are essential to societies.
- Certain societies have *civil rights,* such as the belief in equality or the right not to be discriminated against. These can be legal rights as well.
- Then there are *human rights,* which some argue should be held by every man, woman, and child regardless of nationality. These include the right not to be tortured, the right to security in one's social surroundings, or the right to health and well-being.
- *Freedom rights* include the right to privacy, right to worship as you please, and the right to choose your own friends. The problem is that some people feel they have a right not to be interfered with no matter how obnoxious or dangerous their behavior is.
- Then there are *entitlement rights,* or the rights to lay claim to legitimate goods, a decent job, or good health care.

Rights can be categorized as negative and positive. *Negative rights* refer to freedoms to do certain things and freedom from interference. An example might be freedom to act, think, and speak freely, especially free from government interference. *Positive rights* are claims made on the state to do certain things. Examples might include protection from assault, theft, and invasion of privacy (Appiah, 2003; Baggini & Fosl, 2007).

It is said that rights come with responsibilities. You receive benefits from civil and social order, and in return you give back certain goods and services. This should apply to those who have the ability to meet such obligations (Baggini & Fosl, 2007). All our rights have to balance against the infringement on others or justice in general (Solomon, 1993). Finally, no discussion of rights would be complete without noting that if anyone claims a right, then one has to ask whether such a claimed right imposes a duty on others (Whyte, 2005).

However, all these statements simply assert positions and do not adequately argue for them. The problem is that simply asserting something is not sufficient. Something of this magnitude needs a thoughtful set of premises. So how might a critical thinking case be constructed to further strengthen this principle?

First, let's ask some questions. Consider what would become of ethics if rights were discarded. How could bias-free ethical decisions be made? Whose rights would be respected and whose rights would be disregarded? And once a fundamental right was somehow compromised, what might then occur to other rights? As you can see, some good critical thinking questions strengthen the position for the fundamental rights of all. Now to the argument.

The need for basic human rights is a deeply important, necessary building block in modern ethics (premise). Without rights, no case could reasonably be made for a fair ethical treatment of individuals (premise). Therefore, basic human rights are necessary for fair ethical human conduct (conclusion).

RESPECT FOR PERSONS

Essentially, this holds that we are all endowed with worth and dignity. As such, we are therefore deserving of respect. This applies across the board regardless of a person's social status, gender, ethnicity, sexual orientation, cognitive functioning, or other characteristics. Ethical issues here could involve using people as a means to an end (as noted by Kant) or withholding treatment because one does not respect another's integrity. Clearly this principle is one directed at discrimination of any kind— toward a person, a community, or a culture.

Being respectful has an added element in that such behavior promotes social justice. In addition, it would have you obligate yourself to both be fair and to not discriminate in your work. So it entails duty, as will be seen in many of the upcoming principles.

Using some critical thinking, let us build a short argument where the conclusion is that respect for people should be in this list of ethical principles. One premise to support this conclusion might include that without this level of respect, we risk bias. Bias, as we know, confounds neutrality, which was a stated need for quality ethical decision making. In addition, lack of respect for an individual or group evokes favoritism, which also confounds quality ethical decision making. So now we have an additional argument for the conclusion that respect for persons needs to be on this list.

However, just for the sake of argument (which is, after all, what this book is about), would there ever be a situation in which an addiction counselor should *not* abide by this principle, and such an action would not ethically breach the principle? Does the universal application of the principle in any way water down other ethical standards? Just for the sake of argument, are there people who have more worth and dignity than others? Is it ethically right to equate the dignity and worth of a notable figure with that of a child rapist? Are humans, addiction counselors in particular, really able to apply this evenly across the broad spectrum of humanity they face?

AUTONOMY

Our clients have the right to make their own decisions. Moreover, they are considered to have the ability to make such decisions. Both rights and decision making are the foundation of the ethical principle of *autonomy*. Essentially, this rides the coattails of respect in as much as we (addiction professionals) are not to impose treatments on clients. So it appears that autonomy involves an issue of imposition. Does one impose treatment on those who clearly need it but nonetheless refuse it? The prevailing view is no, we don't do that because it would be unethical because of this respect for a person's autonomy.

Our critical thinking argument for autonomy is that it should be in the list of ethical principles (conclusion) because clients have a right to this principle (premise), and clients are considered capable of making their own decisions (the other premise).

Of course, this gets complicated in terms of cultural values that may not place as much emphasis on autonomy as Western cultures do. Some cultures may need input from family members, religious leaders, or community elders before instituting any particular type of treatment. Yet the principle of autonomy clearly rests on clients being able to make decisions for themselves, which is the conclusion. The first premise is that we have the right and the ability to make decisions for ourselves. It is the second premise that creates some ambiguity. The fly in the soup for this last premise is the question of how capable some of our clients are to make their own decisions.

Consider that we have made provisions for those conditions where clients are not deemed able to make such decisions. For example, despite their protests, we may hospitalize them. The ethics in these situations clearly speaks to safety for the client or community at large. So we seem to be faced with an ethical spectrum issue. At what point does one allow a client to make an autonomous decision for him or herself, and at what point do we take his or her autonomy away? For good measure, consider how a client's age might factor into your thinking.

COMPASSION

Ethically we need to include this in our judgments and decision making. Recall that a while back we mentioned the need for an ethical perspective. Not only does it allow a wide view of things, but it also allows us to place ourselves in a victim's position to see elements of an ethical situation we might otherwise miss. Compassion is similar. It means to suffer with a recipient of an ethical wrongdoing, to see what he sees, and feel what he feels. Compassion, therefore, adds needed benefits to ethical addiction judgments.

The critical thinking argument for inclusion of this principle in the list of ethical standards may be a bit weak. There are no stated requirements of rights or duties that apply to compassion. However, it assists empathy, which in turn may improve the quality of ethical decision making. Hence, the improved quality of decision making provided by compassion necessitates its inclusion on this list.

However, compassion can be confused with sympathy, and sympathy has strong elements of pity. Pity will bias, as will too much compassion. In many of these principles, we are arguing against bias-producing elements that will compromise our ability to make clear judgments. When addressing this particular principle, moderation is in order.

Think about the following questions. Are there situations where compassion would do more harm than good in an ethical decision-making situation? Or said a slightly different way, can and should compassion be a guiding light in all ethical situations? Could an argument be made that compassion is not ethically needed or required in moral judgments and decision making?

CONFIDENTIALITY

Confidentiality is considered a privilege (due to legal restrictions) not an inherent right. It requires addiction professionals not to disclose treatment-related information to third parties without a client's consent. Of course, this can be overturned by certain laws or court orders. The central issue in this case is one of information protection.

Why would information given in counseling sessions be granted protection, and what does it have to do with ethics? There are several reasons. One has to do with the stigma associated with addiction. It goes without saying that many behaviors associated with active addiction can sometimes be seen as shameful and unacceptable to the community or general public. As clients begin the recovery process, they often review their past active addiction behaviors and share such behaviors with a counselor. They do this for several reasons: to gain perspective from what was to what can be. They do it for their own confessional reasons, which can help wipe the slate clean, and for a sense of relief from potential relapse-promoting shame and guilt. All this tender information needs to be protected so it doesn't fall into the wrong hands and do unintended damage to the client, which is a clear ethical issue.

Criminal activity disclosure while a client is in treatment seems to be a long-standing grey area and one of degree. That makes the ethics grey as well. It might be safe to say that not every last detail of a counseling session needs to be shared with a probation officer or judge. To do so could be seen as an ethical breach of confidentiality. On the other hand, the issue of degree or pattern of a client's behavior might warrant a disclosure. Repeated positive urine screens, for example, or severe criminal behavior, would put the ethical responsibility on the shoulders of the counselor to report such behavior to a supervisor or probation officer despite the protests of the client.

Finally, there is the moral issue of confidentiality. When someone tells you very personal, private information, that information is assumed to be offered in a state of trust. Sharing such trusted information without consent could be construed as breaching trust if not creating harm to the client and the professional relationship, both of which are clear ethical issues.

So the critical thinking argument for including confidentiality in the list of ethical standards might be something like this: While mainly a privilege, confidentiality should remain an ethical standard because of the trust factor associated with it. Breaches of trust without consent are deemed unethical and such breaches can and will do some level of harm to the client and professional relationship.

PRIVACY

This principle is certainly related to confidentiality, but it is also distinct. While confidentiality commands clinicians not to disclose treatment information, privacy centers on the right to be free from intrusions, unless given permission. This applies to one's physical body, space, personal data, and even mind. The ethical issue here is one of intrusion, imposition, or infringement without permission. This definitely applies to counseling and our clients, and it is mainly to clients that we apply this principle.

To get a clear picture of privacy, ask some questions. For example, is it ethically and morally appropriate to impose a belief, even a good clinical one, on a client in a session if the client does not wish such an intrusion? Is it ethical or morally appropriate to infringe or breach a client's personal space by getting close, uncomfortably close, during a session with the intent of making a point? Just because someone is in your treatment program, does that automatically allow you to defy a client's privacy in the name of honesty and treatment advancement?

Certainly as addiction counselors, we will be allowed into a client's private world. Yet this condition revolves around the words *allowed* or *invited*. The point of this principle rests on the right to privacy, and unwanted intrusions into body, mind, and private information. (For those who would argue that treatment interventions disregard rights of clients in the name of sobriety, please build your argument and publish it so a critical dialogue can proceed.)

So a quick critical thinking argument for including privacy in the basic ethical principles would be as follows: Privacy is an ethical standard of being free from intrusion and imposition. Failing to respect this standard is to intrude on a person's rights; therefore to intrude is to breach the right to be free from intrusion and imposition.

Yet should the privacy of a client ever be justified? What circumstances, if any, would warrant such an imposition? We generally know the accepted answers to those questions. For example the *Tarasoff v. Regents of California* (Cal.3d 425 [1976]) decision stated that mental health professionals have a duty to protect individuals who are threatened with bodily harm from clients. Do we need to include other exceptions?

TRUTH TELLING

Here we move from rights and intrusion to ethical duty. Telling the truth can be a positive duty (i.e., it is your duty to be honest) and a negative duty (i.e., you should not lie or deceive your clients or others). Should you obtain informed consent from your client, for example, you should (note *should*) fully disclose all health and addiction information you have gathered to your client even though some of it might have a possible negative affect on the client. The duty here is not to misrepresent or withhold information from those who have a legitimate right to it. So using critical thinking, we note the conclusion is truth telling, and the reason you have a duty to this action is because clients and others have a right to it.

Certainly, the question arises whether certain information should be shared if it would not be in the best interests of the client. This is one of those rare situations where you would have to decide if such truth telling would ethically turn out to be harmful in some way. To achieve this, one would have to detail what are the best interests of a client and what kind of information might be disclosed. It is akin to Kant's example of a known murderer asking you the whereabouts of an intended victim. To translate to the addiction field, would truth telling always be the best course of action? Could a situation arise where truth telling might be unethical or morally wrong?

NONMALEFICENCE

We end this section with two important and overarching addiction ethics principles. The first is nonmaleficence, a fancy term for "do no harm" (in Latin *primum non nocere*). It is a duty, *your duty*, not to create, institute, or invoke harm for a client in the course of your interactions. This standard requires that you pay close attention, and not be careless, about what you say and do with clients. It encourages addiction professionals to consider the possible harm that any intervention might cause. It also applies to unintended harm, as in a statement or behavior from you that unintentionally results in harm. For example, inadvertently using disparaging language to emphasize a point, describe a behavior, or situation could cause harm. Certainly, nonmaleficence applies to intentional harm, which is extraordinarily unethical.

Applying our critical thinking argument (and this is not complex at all) is that our conclusion is do no harm, and the reasons are that you have a duty to this principle, and that to do harm is intrinsically immoral.

BENEFICENCE

Beneficence is also a duty. It involves your duty to try to bring about benefits to your clients and make the decisions that are best for the client, without personal gain or in the interests of others. Essentially it requires you to do good and avoid evil and refrain from putting your interests above those of the client. Makes sense.

Let's take a closer look at this last element for a second. With the advancements in addiction research, this last duty allows addiction counselors to bring to the counseling session more benefit, in terms of treatment, than ever thought possible. And in some ways, that places additional obligations on the addiction counselor to really know these new treatment advancements so they can be conveyed to the client. It also forces counselors to confront the coercion element that some counselors have used in the name of beneficence. In this case, we have to assess what level of coercion is beneficence and what is harm.

In addition to the previously listed items, there are other beneficence elements (Manuel & Forcehimes, 2008). Some of these elements recommend that addiction counselors use accurate empathy during their counseling sessions, genuinely interact with their clients, display the right amount of warmth, and use empirically based addiction treatments. Moreover, an addiction counselor should openly discuss what the therapeutic relationship is about, what the financial arrangements are (if any), and what the confidentiality limits are at the very beginning of treatment. All of this and other treatment guidelines should be put into words so that clients can easily understand what they are getting into.

Our critical thinking argument here is to propose that beneficence (do good) is an ethical standard (conclusion) because to do good implies high ethical qualities, while to do evil is without question unethical. Again, simple and straightforward.

JUSTICE

Justice for our purposes is seen as an overarching concept that has applications to all of the eight principles we just reviewed. So it deserves its own section. Justice can be seen as a primary virtue (Solomon, 1993). There are different forms of justice. Often seen as punitive or corrective, it acknowledges a person's right to due process, fair compensation for harm done, and a fair distribution of benefits (Vaughn, 2008). It also can more often be seen as the attitude that guides moral rightness and impartiality. Justice can be seen as that which assigns blame and punishment. Generally this is called *retributive justice* (Solomon, 1993). Finally, there is *distributive justice,* which has to do with allotment of goods, as a matter of reward, and accordance with what one deserves (Solomon, 1993).

Justice needs to be a guiding principle in an addiction treatment program for a number of reasons. As an example, clients are expected to be addressed with justice as it applies to fairness in treatment planning and treatment selection. Moreover, justice will be served if the program staff is fair in its assessments and performs them with as little bias as possible. Finally, addiction clients who breach program rules will be served with justice if they are not capriciously discharged based only on hearsay or strong emotions or unwarranted bias. Rather, such cases will be reviewed and examined with impartiality and fair treatment.

Our critical thinking argument here is to propose that justice is an overriding ethical principle in that it is based on the premises of moral rightness, impartiality, and that which is just, which are also considered guidelines. These are conditions found within or apart from the many, if not all, other ethical principles.

THE LEAST YOU NEED TO KNOW

All these addiction principles constitute the ethical backbone of our field. To view them in graphic form, see Figure 12.1.

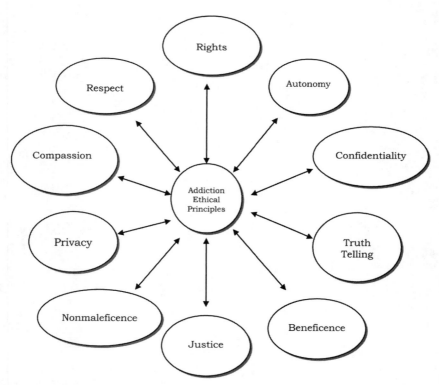

Figure 12.1 Core ethical addiction principles.

13 Some Practical Guidelines

We have spent quite a bit of time discussing ethical models, critical thinking principles, ethical fallacies, and general addiction ethics principles. All of that was rather broad. Well, it's about time to narrow the focus and take a look at some specific addiction ethics concerns. We examine what they are, and put forward a few solid arguments to avoid them. Finally, we sketch a list of ethical behaviors that come too close for comfort. This means that those of you who tread close to these behaviors are forewarned to be cautious, because you are getting too close to an ethical violation.

COMMON ETHICAL VIOLATIONS

To set the stage for this chapter, let's start with a few lists of common ethical violations committed by various human service providers. They come from the fields of psychology, counseling, and addiction.

First, from psychology, Bernstein and Hartsell (2000) noted a list of eight in order of frequency.

- Sexual exploitation
- Dual relationships

- Boundary violations
- Breach of confidentiality
- Fraudulent billing
- Financial client exploitation
- Providing services while impaired
- Statute reporting violations

Complaints received against licensed professional counselors include the following (Neukrug, 1999):

- Practicing without a license
- Sexual relationship with a client
- Inappropriate fee assessment (e.g., insurance fraud)
- Dual relationships
- Confidentiality breach
- Failure to report abuse (e.g., child, spouse)

As for the addiction field, St. Germaine (1997) reviewed the records of 55 certification boards to survey ethical complaints. She found the most common complaints consisted of the following:

- Having sexual relationships with current clients
- Providers unable to practice with skill/safety because of drug or alcohol use or other mental or physical conditions
- Practicing without a certificate

We will now look at some of these in more detail.

BOUNDARY ISSUES

One cannot help notice that some type of boundary violation cropped up on all three lists. Perhaps it is a good time to address this noticeable problem. To begin, we first differentiate between degrees of boundary issues. Two such degrees are to be noted: *boundary crossings* and *boundary violations* (Johnson & Ridley, 2008; Manuel & Forcehimes, 2008). Both are considered transgressions. Crossings are judged as minor, which might include starting sessions late, or ending too early. Another crossing is not setting limits on client contact outside sessions (such as what constitutes emergency calls versus social calls). If you maintain a professional relationship with your clients, crossings generally will not occur.

Violations on the other hand are major transgressions. An example of this is a counselor's disclosure of personal information that provides no clinical value, or doesn't benefit a client, and may only serve the counselor. Spending way too much time with a particular client or giving a particular client too much special attention is another violation example. Certainly dual relationships fall into this category. Finally, there is the example of a counselor who overidentifies with a client to the extent that his or her clinical judgment becomes impaired. For example, a counselor might begin to believe a client needs a high dose of whatever treatment personally worked for the counselor himself, and then he will lose track of alternative methods that could be as effective if not more so. That is an ethical issue. The same could apply to a counselor who overidentifies with a client on, say, a childhood or depression issue, then blocks out other perhaps more accurate assessments. One way to keep this crossing and violation thing straight is that violations generally exploit or harm the client, which is a nonmaleficence issue.

In terms of critical thinking, note that the key issue is the harm that can result from identifying too closely with a client, which can impair clinical judgment. Counselors who insist on seeing no harm with overidentification would have to build an argument for their position. This would require at least one premise, including some facts and data, and a moral element to support the conclusion. This would be an interesting argument.

One last note is needed on the boundary issues. Some supervisors insist you keep your boundaries very clear, perhaps to the point of being emotionless if not sterile. In this manner, you certainly avoid any possibility of boundary crossings or lawsuits. The question then is how ethical is it to become so overprotected so as to lose possible warmth needed in the relationship-building phase of therapy?

ADDICTION COUNSELORS IN RECOVERY

There are a few ethical issues that recovering addictions counselors may face that others might not. For example, how much (if anything) does one disclose about one's personal recovery? Too much disclosure, it is argued, could create a more personal, less formal, less professional relationship (Manuel & Forcehimes, 2008). Such degrees of unprofessionalism could begin to challenge ethical boundaries.

But if you think about it, the same set of elements certainly applies to the so-called nonrecovering counselors. Nonrecovering counselors could disclose too much personal information about their childhood or personal problems, and perhaps believe the process they used to achieve mental health would work well for their clients to the exclusion of other equally if not more effective interventions.

Other ethical dilemmas for the recovering counselor include encountering clients at self-help meetings. One ethical issue here is anonymity. If, for example, a counselor attends a self-help group, and sees an active client, but never disclosed his own addiction to that client, the counselor's anonymity is then broken. Another problem for the counselor might be in terms of disclosing personal information at such a meeting, and what impact such information might have on the next session with the client. The ethical point, you might argue, would have to do with how such information might unintentionally influence the professional relationship.

LIMITS OF PROFESSIONAL EXPERTISE (SCOPE OF PRACTICE)

Knowing your professional limits is a big ethical issue. The ethical concern here is giving a client advice on issues where your expertise is inadequate. This includes advice on taking medications, or giving medical recommendations when you don't have a medical degree. It also includes conducting treatment in areas where you feel short on training. For example, we see a lot of clients who have co-occurring disorders. Now such disorders can cover a wide range of issues beyond mental health issues. They can include case management problems (housing, disability, insurance forms, etc.) or family problems, among others. Yet some addiction counselors step right into these uncharted waters as if they know what they are talking about. This is an ethical no-no. Addiction counselors have to know their limits.

A deductive-type argument for keeping within your professional limits might be something like.

Offering treatment services in an area of clinical treatment beyond your expertise level can cause damage.

Causing harm to clients flies in the face of the ethical principle of nonmaleficence.

Therefore, offering treatment services beyond one's professional expertise is unethical.

THE ETHICS OF HARM REDUCTION

Miller (2008) has outlined the central factors for the harm reduction ethical argument. Essentially, harm reduction is a pragmatic approach. Its main focus is to minimize harm that comes from risky substance use behavior. It works on the general principle of *gradualism,* which encourages measured steps toward reducing risk and improving health. This principle is a stark contrast to zero tolerance or total abstinence approaches.

In many circles, harm reduction is often associated with controlled drinking. These circles argue against harm reduction because they feel that clients in early recovery do not have the decision-making ability to make such choices. Finally, these circles argue, if harm reduction is left unchecked, it could spread and hold back people from seeking treatment.

It needs to be noted that an argument against the use of the harm reduction centers on nonmoral premises of the syllogism.

Any treatment position that harms people is unethical.

Many people are harmed by adhering to the principles of harm reduction (the nonmoral premise).

Harm reduction is therefore unethical.

This is a prime example of what stirs ethical problems. The nonmoral premise is one that implies potential harm waits for substance abuse clients who could or would be harmed by listening to the so-called propaganda of harm reduction and subsequently relapsing or not even beginning treatment because of its position. However, the point is that there is little if any data to support this contention (Miller, 2008). What some abstinence-based counselors, authors, and others are doing is speculating as to what *might* happen. In order to substantiate their speculation, they need data to back their claims.

While this little discussion certainly does not resolve this contentious debate, it will be left to the reader to press for other ethical perspectives and critical thinking elements to apply.

ETHICAL WARNING SIGNS

Here is a list of ethical issues that tread too close for comfort in terms of posing potential ethical problems. They are posted as ethical warning signs. Should you relate to some of them, they shout, "You are getting too close for comfort." "Back away, there is ethical trouble ahead." Many were taken from Bernstein and Hartsell (2000), and adapted for addiction ethics.

Discrimination

Discrimination, in addiction counseling or the general human service field, is about as egregious a no-no as you can get. It means you are showing prejudice against a client or group of clients for whatever reason. A critical thinking argument on this runs some thing like:

Offering unequal services to clients is to offer disparate services to clients.

Disparate services could potentially withhold the best treatment available to a client.

Withholding best treatment would not be doing your duty to help the client.

Not doing your duty to help the client flies in the face of the principle of beneficence and is considered unethical.

Moreover, one client or group of clients has the same right to equal services as any other client or groups of clients.

Not to offer what is right for a client is wrong.

Therefore, discriminating against a client or groups of clients is unethical.

Don't minimize a discrimination complaint. This is too close for comfort, and if the minimization were ever made public, it might well spell your downfall. Consider that to minimize such an issue could be construed as a cover-up. Such actions have ethical overtones.

Misleading Statements

Whether you work for yourself or in a program, you need to be careful that what you say to consumers is accurate and not deceptive. For example, implying in an advertisement that your treatment provides more positive outcome results when no data supports such a claim is getting too close for comfort. It especially gets too close for comfort if such ads are promulgated just for the sake of increasing admissions.

Misleading statements can also present you in a professional light that is not accurate. For example, embellishing your resume with more experience or training is getting too close for comfort. Why?

Embellishing experience or training on your resume gives a false impression.

False impressions are designed to mislead a potential employer, and that is unethical.

Therefore, implying you have certain experiences or trainings that you do not really have is unethical.

Finally, for this case, you the professional are accountable for your actions as to what you say and what you write. How you present yourself to a prospective employer, a client, and colleagues is your sole responsibility. And while some professionals are eager for success, or financial reward, to assuage their damaged integrity or deflated ego, responsibility always entails an element of ethics (Johnson & Ridley, 2008).

Informed Consent

Informed consent is a process that is intended to fully inform clients about what to expect before they enter treatment. Simply put, it is a prerequisite for treatment. It covers a number of important points the client should know before he signs on the dotted line. These key factors include: risks, limits, costs, time frames, and right to refuse, among others. Getting too close for comfort on this issue might include not adequately informing the client of what is to come.

Capacity to Understand Informed Consent

All clients must read and understand what they are about to get into when it comes to addiction treatment. An ethical informed consent close call might include assuming the client understands or nods his head in agreement when in fact he or she doesn't, or he might even be mildly intoxicated or in some level of withdrawal. The intoxicated issue seems easy enough to resolve, but what of the client who states that he or she understands but doesn't and then later accuses you of deception. What steps might you take to assure yourself that the client indeed does understand what he is getting into?

Referring Clients

Sending clients off to a referral is meant as a benefit. However, accepting any kickback, or having conflicts of interest, is questionable in terms of ethics. In addition, the referral source should have the competency necessary to handle the referral in question, as in a specialized dual disorders program. Just to simply refer a client to another program without knowledge of its expertise, which could do potential harm, is getting too close for comfort.

Interviewing

Written case formulations or clinical impressions that do not include sensible interviewing techniques (e.g., standardized questionnaires, valid test instruments) may be getting too close for comfort. Using valid questionnaires and tests improves the quality of an interview and can eliminate the appearance of bias.

An addiction counselor who is asked to testify concerning a client or give a clinical impression, but who has not had personal contact with said client, is getting too close for comfort.

To provide secondary evidence from an addiction magazine or newsletter, or third-person opinions, might clarify your clinical impression, but the interview proper is the definitive factor in determining such an impression. To rely too heavily on secondary evidence comes too close for comfort.

Professional Development and Continuing Education

Addiction professionals have the obligation to keep current with the latest treatment developments (Taleff, 2005). If an improved treatment technique is known and not used, the addiction professional is involved in an unethical practice. Why? Using the critical thinking (deductive) argument approach, the logic might look like this:

> The addiction professional is aware that he has the responsibility of keeping himself informed and current as to better-quality treatments because not being aware of such modalities risks doing harm.
>
> In addiction treatment, to risk harm is unethical.
>
> Therefore, not staying current with clinical practices in addiction treatment settings is unethical.

People You Don't Do Therapy With

If there is a good chance that objectivity would be compromised with a client, you may be getting too close to the ethical edge. This is especially true if the prospective client is a relative or associate. You avoid this edge if the only relationship between you and the client is a therapeutic one.

Rather than risk an ethical problem, use the following rule: When in doubt, do not accept a client into therapy.

Problematic Treatments

You should approach some treatments available on the market with caution. These kinds of so-called treatments just do not have data to support their use. They also come with warnings that using them can make individuals worse. To ignore such warnings may incur ethical problems. An abbreviated list of such treatments includes the following (Lilienfeld, 2007):

- Critical incident stress debriefing. Often prescribed after trauma of any kind (e.g., combat, airplane accident, terrorist attack), it has been shown to be ineffective and may cause harm in come cases.
- Grief counseling. This is often looked on as a critical need by many professionals, especially regarding a loss of a loved one. However, some clients fare worse after it is used.
- Peer group work for conduct disorder. This is often used with children and adolescents, but some research has found a worsening effect following such group work.

- Scared straight or boot camps. These attempt to address conduct-disordered adolescents with various tough interventions. While intuitively appealing, no research to date supports their efficacy.
- Repressed memory therapy. This refers to a group of procedures used to unearth repressed childhood trauma. Given the intense psychological and legal debates over the veracity of repressed memories, it is best to distance yourself from this concept. Enough said.
- Attachment therapies. This includes rebirthing and reparenting. Research shows these are simply not effective and in some cases dangerous.
- Facilitated communication. These are strategies used to converse with autistic children through facilitators (who hold the hands of children over a computer keyboard). Unfortunately, there is little to no research in support for these techniques.

Not Terminating Treatment

Keeping a client in treatment when the client no longer benefits from it is getting too close for comfort. This is especially true if the decision is made because the client is a source of steady reimbursement or if the practitioner continues to use a therapy that is not working. Holding a client in treatment for anything other than solid treatment reasons is too close for comfort.

Not Knowing the Ethical Codes

Ignorance of ethical codes is no excuse. Counselors are required to know them.

Record Keeping

As much as most counselors dislike documentation, it is a basic rule of treatment. To be careless about record keeping is unprofessional and way too close for comfort.

Counselor Impairment

Counselors must function effectively in their daily work. To be impaired (e.g., using prescription drugs, alcohol, or being distracted by family responsibilities) on the job is getting too close for comfort. Such impairment dilutes counseling effectiveness. Integrity dictates you know your limits in terms of fatigue, burnout, or impairment (Johnson & Ridley, 2008).

Confidentiality Exceptions

Certain issues found in treatment (sexual abuse) must be legally disclosed by law. A counselor must be knowledgeable of such exceptions. Not to divulge something heard in treatment that should be revealed is way too close for comfort.

Duty to Warn

Client threats to harm a third party should be taken seriously. The problem is that there are no clear, mandated duty to warn codes in the United States. Hence, know your state laws, and consider contacting law enforcement officials if you feel you cannot contact the potential victim. To be on the safe side, contact your state licensing or certification board for direction. Not to do any so is getting too close for comfort.

Turf Battles

Bad mouthing a competitor is getting too close for comfort, especially if made public. Just don't do it.

Your Professional Vulnerability

Vulnerability generally means you are becoming susceptible to personal feelings in the counseling relationship. If there is even a hint of growing personal connection between you and a client, immediately set the record straight, explain professional boundaries, and document the event and how it was handled. To ignore this is getting too close for comfort.

Supervision

The clinical relationship between supervisor and supervisee is based on clinical objectivity and clear boundaries and should not be compromised by dual relationships. Moreover, exploitation in any manner, even the slightest, is still exploitation, and that is getting way too close for comfort.

Administration

Administrators who increase the workload on counselors to the point of overload, as in insisting on excessive caseloads, just to increase income are getting too close for comfort.

Forensic Work

All forensic counseling work, assessment, treatment, and referral should be handled with extreme caution and care. You are operating in the realm of legal consequences, and your work will be scrutinized. Thus, to downplay such work or do sloppy work in this area may well have consequences for your professional career.

Confidentiality in Group Therapy

Group therapy is the workhorse of the addiction treatment field. Much personal information and history is shared in that therapeutic mode. Such personal information warrants protection and respect. Before you start a group, thoroughly and completely discuss confidentiality with all group members. While a guarantee of confidentiality cannot be made, that lack of confidentiality should be shared with the members. To be on the safe side, make sure all members sign a written commitment to safeguard all that is heard. To do otherwise is to get too close for comfort.

Mediocrity

This is directed at those addiction professionals who do just enough to get by and precious little else. They always operate at minimal standards and rarely ever breach ethical codes. Moreover, they do what they have to and no more in terms of educating themselves. They attend workshops for recertification but probably haven't read a professional book in years. So their overall work just passes minimal standards. They never excel or strive for excellence. While they do not violate the letter of the law, ethically they may fall short on the spirit of the law, which is getting too close for comfort.

This is the place where "The Least You Need to Know" chapter summary is usually placed. However, that just does not seem to fit at the end of this chapter. So we end with the following.

WHAT IS THE BEST JUDGMENT YOU CAN PRODUCE?

- Are you sure the judgments you cited for these many ethical problems are the finest you could flesh out?
- Consider assessing addiction ethics issues not listed here and building a formal argument to support your position using *the addiction ethics judgment kit.*

14 Caveats in Ethical Thinking

Any good book on critical thinking, ethics, and morality needs to come with a set of warnings about ethical decision making. Essentially, all this talk about different morals standards, positions, and critical thinking can be used in bad ways. This chapter will examine some common abuses of ethics.

POWER

One of the bad ways ethics can be abused is from the lure of power, and it is placed first. Why? Because in a spirited ethical debate, or when one takes a moral stance, such a debate or stance can sometimes come with an air of smugness and righteousness, if not a feeling of power. The kind of power we are talking about is one of, "I defeated your position" or "I made you retreat and showed you up." Some folks misuse ethical debate not for clarity, fairness, and equality, but for this kind of power.

Next, while survey data is lacking on this issue, it is assumed that addiction counselors at some level know they have power. It comes in a variety of forms (Pope & Vasquez, 2007). Some addiction counselors are licensed psychologists or state-certified counselors. With such recognition comes the power to do therapy that cannot be done without such recognition. We have power by virtue of our ability to name and define problems and behaviors (diagnosing). This gives us power because of the influence it can and will have on clients.

We have people-changing knowledge. By virtue of our training and education, we specialize in influencing clients in terms of their decisions and actions. We thus hold potential sway over our clients' lives. If improperly used, this power can exploit. The same holds true for the power of expectation many clients have toward our abilities to help them change. We are invested, like it or not, with power to bring about change. We are given power to do things ordinary people are forbidden to do. We are paid to intrude into a client's deepest, darkest secrets. We have power to influence a client's behavior in terms of rewards or disproving frowns.

Finally, there is the differential power element. This is built into therapy through our position and our supposed expert status. People come to us expecting (perhaps) to be in a secondary role. We do the questioning, and the client is on the receiving end of our questions, which definitely creates a power differential. If one abuses these power elements, it becomes an ethical issue.

OBEDIENCE AND POWER

All laws of society and religious doctrines promote some element of obedience to a set of practices, social welfare, or public good, and all heighten the element of power. Someone who has the ability to impose or recommend morals may not have your best interests in mind. They may have their own best interests in mind. They may see the possibility of using a code of ethics or commandments to control the recipients of the code. It is the abuse of ethics for power and control through obedience. Power needs to control and will often use whatever means necessary to facilitate that control, even using ethics or morals to achieve that end.

ARROGANCE

Note the superiority and arrogance that comes with people who abuse ethics for their own ends. They cite the superiority of their morality over yours. (This view can be held by members of all types of religious, political, or other groups.) Again, it is a power move meant to demean not only your moral position, but often you. That is, it comes in the form of a personal attack. Hell hath no fury like a righteous moralist aroused (Kurtz, 2007).

LAST WARNINGS

Sadly, ethics can be manipulated by people who:

- Are narrow-minded and angry and use these tendencies to manipulate others.
- Are manipulative and abuse ethics in order to be right.
- Consider themselves superior to others.
- Enforce rules simply to avenge themselves on their enemies.

Some would say we are very much in a moral age, not one of moral decay. This presents a problem because strong moral attitudes are intolerant, and intolerance is one of the worst discourtesies (Grayling, 2002). Hence, note the lack of civility in today's moral arguments—especially from the moralizers.

There is one final caveat: There is always a price to pay for ethical decisions (or for that matter any decision). Any decision, even the best-made one, can lead to unforeseen consequences. The only defense is to use the best thought possible at the time of the decision.

Let us not end with a bad taste in our mouths. There are many exciting elements of understanding moral positions and critical thinking skills. These can and will allow the fresh air of new thought to come into your mind. By knowing a bit of philosophy and critical thinking, you will no longer take authority for granted. It will challenge you to take close note of ambiguities and assumptions, and questionable claims of morals and ethics. It will keep you from being carried along with any drift of opinion that comes down the pike. And it will have you requesting clarification and reasons for addiction ethics arguments and claims.

Mostly it will have you call the bluff of accepted dogma and take a stand (Woodhouse, 1994).

THE LEAST YOU NEED TO KNOW

- Be aware of the various forms of power that can be used against well-crafted ethical judgment and decision making.
- Now put to use all you have read, and make it a more ethical field for all of us.

Appendix: Practice Situations

Here is a list of ethical practice situations. Much of the inspiration for the situations came from ICRC (1994, 1999), and NAADAC (1994). Each asks you to make an ethical judgment. Recall all the ideas and strategies that have been provided in the book, and utilize them in your response.

MISLEADING STATEMENTS

On her resume for a potential inpatient drug and alcohol counseling position, Cindy lists that she has recently graduated from a local university with a psychology degree, which is accurate. She lists under her past experiences that she worked in a drug and alcohol program for a year and conducted counseling. In reality, this was an internship and not a very good one at that. During the year, Cindy mostly answered the phone on the 3 P.M.–11 P.M. shift and filed charts. On many evenings, she did chat with clients in the program's lounge, but technically this was not considered treatment. Cindy is eager to work in the field and feels wording her resume in this manner might increase her chances for being hired.

Is there a point or level when seemingly innocent exaggerations become ethical problems even if for good reasons? In terms of this situation, what would you consider such a point at which Cindy crossed the line, and what advice would you give her? Build a deductive argument for and against the ethical possibility.

TALKING TO THE MEDIA

Authors, workshop presenters, and others have an obligation to speak to the press in a responsible manner and with the aim of informing the public about addiction. So consider the following example. An author who recently published an addiction treatment book is asked by a local TV reporter to answer a few questions about the success rate for addiction treatment. Now the reporter is interested in recovery and has no idea the same practitioner has written a book. Yet the author knows that publicity (especially TV) will certainly garner more book sales. So while answering the questions, the author injects that he has just published a book on the subject. He says that his recent book "is a quantum step forward in treating addiction." However, the book offers no more than the usual traditional treatment theories and strategies. The reporter indicates on the 6 o'clock news that the author states he has a book that makes all others look old-fashioned. Is the author obligated to set the record straight about his book, or can he let the misinformation possibly supply a few more book sales? Build a deductive argument for and against the ethical possibility.

CONFIDENTIALITY

Following the attendance of an addiction workshop on alcohol abuse and bipolar disorder, two participants from different treatment programs begin discussing the fine points of the presentation over coffee. One participant begins to describe a current active client, attempting to connect ideas presented in the workshop, to the other participant. Without mentioning the client's name or other information other than the client's symptoms, has this participant breached the client's confidentiality? Build a deductive argument for and against the ethical possibility.

DISCRIMINATION

Robert is a staunch Republican and is often heard talking conservative politics around the lunch table. He is, however, an able and competent addiction counselor. Presently, he is working with a client (Elizabeth) who is an avowed Democrat. They both know each other's political affiliations. Elizabeth knows of Robert's politics because she has seen a photo in the local newspaper of Robert shaking a predominant state Republican's hand. Robert knows of Elizabeth's politics because she mentioned them in the initial assessment. These differences have not interfered with therapy, which is progressing well. One day before a session, Elizabeth overhears Robert from the waiting room say something to the effect that he never met a Democrat he ever trusted. How should Elizabeth react in the session that is about to begin, or should she react at all? Can Robert continue to treat Elizabeth without regard to the fact that she is a dedicated Democrat? Build arguments to continue the treatment process and build arguments to end it.

BOUNDARY VIOLATIONS

Counselor Relationship

Two addiction counselors have worked together in the same treatment program for a few years. At first, they had a professional and cordial relationship. Over time, they found a budding friendship growing between them. Now, they often spend time together at lunch, are seen leaving work together, and will spend time then drinking coffee and chatting about the work day. There is no sexual or romantic relationship, save for the companionship they enjoy between them. Yes, they do, however, gossip and sometimes complain about work. Build an argument for and against possible ethical concerns in such a situation.

Bartering

An addiction counselor begins to have problems with her home computer. She soon realizes that she needs computer assistance and calls one of those "come to your home" computer services. In the course of the visit, the technician finds out the profession of the addiction counselor. He begins to reveal that he has a daughter who is having drug problems. The addiction counselor tells the technician that she has handled such cases in the past and thinks she might be able to help. After the counselor's computer is fixed, the technician would like to follow up with the counselor's offer of assistance. However, the technician does not have health insurance and his cash flow is not good at this time. The technician offers an arrangement where he suggests a trade, fixing her computer and continued upkeep in exchange for counseling for his daughter. Build an argument for and against possible ethical concerns in such a situation.

COUNSELOR IMPAIRMENT

A recovering counselor has been under extreme stress at work (excessive caseload and a demanding boss), plus her mother is suffering from a long-term illness that has recently gotten worse. Much of the family responsibility is now being shifted to the counselor's shoulders, adding more stress. Crying and alone, the recovering counselor takes one drink thinking she might get some needed relief. She immediately recognizes this was the wrong thing to do and stops. She tells a fellow counselor in the program. Should the fellow counselor report the situation? What should happen? Build a case.

ETHICAL RESPONSIBILITY 1

If a client relapses following a discharge from an inpatient treatment program, is it ethically responsible for the staff of the program to offer a pat account of the relapse (for example, to claim that the relapse was due to the return of the client's denial)? Is it ethically responsible for the staff to wipe their hands of any blame for the relapse? Build a case for or against such practices.

ETHICAL RESPONSIBILITY 2

Judy, an addiction counselor, conducts an intake interview on a client. She assesses, among other things, that this individual indeed has a serious alcohol problem. She dutifully creates a treatment plan that addresses the main problem (ETOH abuse), then creates a goal and a set of interventions that should be used. The treatment is scheduled to extend over a 3-month period.

Near the beginning of the third month, Judy has not conducted any additional assessments other than noting some dynamics seen in their weekly sessions. At this juncture, the treatment plan remains the same as at admission, and no additional assessment has been conducted. Considering that there may be other important or hidden treatment issues to address, is it ethical for Judy to continue with client information that may be out-of-date? Build an argument for and one against the ethical possibility.

HARM REDUCTION

Whatever your personal take on harm reduction (i.e., attempting to reduce the harm caused by, say, heroin by giving clean syringes to an active heroin user), build a deductive argument for and against the ethics of this intervention.

CONFLICT OF COUNSELOR VALUES

A counselor (Jim), who is a strong supporter of AA, meets a client who does not wish to attend meetings. The client says, "They suck." Such a statement said with such vehemence stings Jim, because he truly believes the AA program saved his life. Jim is visibly upset and intends to approach this client and force him into going to meetings or discharge him if he doesn't comply. As Jim's supervisor, what should you ethically say?

KICKBACK

You have just referred a client to a private practitioner because you believe the private practitioner and the client will be a good fit. Two weeks later, the private practitioner calls and invites you to lunch, "as a token of my appreciation for the referral." Do you take the invitation?

CLINICAL STUBBORNNESS

Harold, a colleague of yours, is a firm believer in confronting clients because he believes that active substance abusers are con artists, and confrontation is *the* preferred method to get clients to become truly aware of their abuse. You hear him harshly confronting a new client. That client reported he used methamphetamine just before he was admitted to your program. What, if anything, do you say to Harold?

ADMINISTRATOR

You work for a small inpatient addiction program. Budgets are always tight, and as the clinical director of the program, you have daily contact with the chief administrator. He has been known to make decisions without consulting staff or taking input. He is known not to like one counselor who works for you. They have had words in the past. The administrator calls you into his office one day and says, "I want that counselor fired. If you don't do it, I will replace you." Build an ethical argument for what you would do.

SUPERVISION

A counselor and a supervisor work at the same addiction program. They soon find they have much in common. They begin to spend a few hours chatting about counseling theories and the latest research ideas, and they have good stimulating conversation. Build an argument for and against possible ethical concerns in such a situation.

CULTURAL ISSUES

Working for the first time with a native population, an addiction counselor finds himself being hugged vigorously following a session as a sign of thanks and respect for his help. However, some previous supervisors and colleagues have told this counselor that touching clients can be seen as a boundary violation and could potentially lead to ethical problems. The counselor feels caught between respecting local cultural norms and potential boundary violations. As a colleague, this counselor asks for your advice. Build an argument for or against continuing to receive such signs of appreciation.

There is one last ethical issue to address. It is an enduring and central addiction ethics problem.

Should someone who does something morally, ethically, or criminally wrong under the influence of substances ever be spared the consequences (prison, for example) of that behavior?

While some people and organizations tend to believe they have the answer to this, I want the reader to build a case for your answer. Previous responses to this question often lack a thinking response. This ethical question cuts to the core of our field and has implications on whether addiction should rightfully be considered a disease. Such a heady response requires more thought and reflection than many others have offered in the past.

Consider some of the following points. On the one hand, some people in the addiction field believe individuals with a severe and active addiction should not be held accountable for their actions. They are considered so possessed by the substances in their system that they cannot and should not be accountable for their actions.

For your consideration, I include brief material from Gazzaniga (2008) on this important question. He notes that freedom can be hampered or limited by either internal or external constraints. Internal constraints, or willpower if you will, might include one's ability to delay gratification. External constraints include cultural or community values that allow a wider or narrower range of allowable drinking behaviors. Both need to be factored into a working premise. Shermer (2004), on the other hand, points out that while freedom may be diminished for a number of reasons, it is never extinguished.

Finally and despite the many discoveries in brain science over the years, such as the importance of neurotransmitters to many mental health issues, it appears that neurotransmitters alone do not explain the loss of control or the capacity to resist substances in an active addiction. Such an explanation has yet to be offered. That's not to say that someday a clear mechanism will never be found. But we do not seem to be at that point, which presses us to answer as best we can with what we have available.

Essentially, this question centers on whether someone with a severe addiction problem loses control so completely (entire loss of freedom) and becomes so overwhelmed by his or her addiction that his or her actions in this state can or should be excused.

Consider using the addiction ethics judgment kit to aid your thinking. Then think about sharing your final judgment with colleagues to get a good dialogue going or, better yet, consider publishing your assessment to get a national dialogue going. Might be interesting.

References

Adler, A. (1954). *Understanding human nature.* Greenwich, CT: Fawcettt. (Original work published 1927)

Allegretti, C. L., & Frederick. J. N. (1995). A model for thinking critically about ethical issues. *Teaching in Psychology, 22*(1), 46–48.

Appiah, K. A. (2003). *Thinking it through: An introduction to contemporary philosophy.* New York: Oxford University Press

Baggini, J., & Fosl, P. S. (2003). *The philosopher's toolkit: A compendium of philosophical concepts and methods.* Malden, MA: Blackwell Publishing.

Baggini, J., & Fosl, P. S. (2007). *The ethics toolkit: A compendium of ethical concepts and methods.* Malden, MA: Blackwell Publishing.

Bandman, E. L., & Bandman, B. (1988). *Critical thinking in nursing.* East Norwalk, CT: Appleton & Lange.

Barad, J., & Robertson, E. (2000). *The ethics of Star Trek.* New York: Pernnial.

Bensley, D. A. (1998). *Critical thinking in psychology: A unified skills approach.* Pacific Grove, CA: Brooks/Cole.

Bernstein, B., & Hartsell, T. L. (2000). *The portable ethicist for mental health professionals: An A-Z guide to responsible practice.* New York: John Wiley & Sons.

Booth, W. C., Colomb, G. G., & Williams, J. M. (1995). *The craft of research.* Chicago: University of Chicago Press.

Bordens, K. S., & Abbott, B. B. (1996). *Research design and method: A process approach.* Mountain View, CA: Mayfield.

Bowell, T., & Kemp, G. (2002). *Critical thinking: A concise guide.* London: Routledge.

Brafman, O., & Brafman, R. (2008). *Sway: The irresistible pull of irrational behavior.* New York: Doubleday.

Brown, M. (1996). *The quest for moral foundations: An introduction to ethics.* Washington, DC: Georgetown University Press.

Brown, M. (2001). *The one-minute philosopher.* Manchester, NH: Sophia Press.

Buchanan, M. (2007). *The social atom.* New York: Bloomsbury.

Burton, R. A. (2008). *On being certain: Believing you're right even when you're not.* New York: St. Martin's Press.

Cannavo, S. (1998). *Think to win: The power of logic in everyday life.* Amherst, NY: Prometheus Books.

Chaffee, J. (2003). *Thinking critically* (7th ed.). Boston: Houghton Mifflin.

Christian, J. L. (1977). *Philosophy: An introduction to the art of wondering* (2nd ed.). New York: Holt, Reinhart, and Winston.

Cohen, R. (2002). *The good, the bad, and the difference.* New York: Broadway Books.

Curtler, H. M. (2004). *Ethical argument: Critical thinking in ethics*. New York: Oxford.

Dewdney, A. K. (1997). *Yes, we have no neutrinos*. New York: Wiley.

Epstein, R. L., & Kernberger, C. (2006). *The pocket guide to critical thinking* (3rd ed.). Belmont, CA: Thomson Wadsworth.

Ethical dilemmas. (2008, July). St. James Ethics Centre. Retrieved January 19, 2009, from http://www.ethics.org.au/about-ethics/ethical-dilemmas/dilemma-08-07.html

Fisher, A. (2001). *Critical thinking: An introduction*. Cambridge, UK: Cambridge University Press.

Ford, G. G. (2006). *Ethical reasoning for mental health professionals*. Thousand Oaks, CA: Sage Publications.

Fox News. (2007). *Coked-up mom gets 9 months in jail for killing daughter with breast milk*. Retrieved from http://www.foxnews.com/printer_friendly_story/0,3566,2507 40,00.html

Gazzaniga, M. S. (2005). *The ethical brain*. New York: Dana Press.

Gazzaniga, M. S. (2008). *Human: The science behind what makes us unique*. New York: Ecco.

Geppert, C. M. A., & Roberts, L. W. (2008). Ethical foundations of substance abuse treatment. In G. M. A. Geppert & L. W. Roberts (Eds.), *The book of ethics: Expert guidance for professionals who treat addiction* (pp. 1–27). Center City, MN: Hazelden.

Grayling, A. C. (2002a). *The meaning of things*. London, England: Phoenix.

Guy, M. E. (1990). *Ethical decision making in everyday work decisions*. New York: Quorum Books.

Haidt, J. (2003). The moral emotions. In R. J. Davidson, K. R. Scherer, & H. H. Goldsmith (Eds.), *Handbook of affective sciences* (pp. 853–870). Oxford: Oxford University Press.

Hallinan, J. T. (2009). *Why we make mistakes*. New York: Broadway Books.

Hare, W. (2009). What open-mindedness requires. *Skeptical Inquirer, 33*(2), 36–39.

Harris, S. (2005). *The end of faith*. New York: Norton.

Honderich, T. (Ed.) (1995). *The Oxford companion of philosophy*. Oxford: Oxford University Press.

Honer, S. M., & Hunt, T. C. (1968). *Invitation to philosophy: An introductory handbook*. Belmont, CA: Wadsworth.

Hospers, J. (1953). *An introduction to philosophical analysis*. New York: Prentice-Hall.

Hughes, W. (2000). *Critical thinking: An introduction to basic skills* (3rd ed.). Peterborough, Ontario, Canada: Broadview.

Hurley, P. J. (1997). *A concise introduction to logic* (6th ed.). Belmont, CA: Wadsworth.

ICRC. (1994). *Prevention ethics standards*. Falls Church, VA: International Certification & Reciprocity Consortium Alcohol and Other Drug Abuse Inc.

ICRC. (1999). *Code of ethics for clinical supervisors*. Falls Church, VA: International Certification & Reciprocity Consortium Alcohol and Other Drug Abuse Inc.

Ingram, D. B., & Parks, J. A. (2002). *The complete idiot's guide to understanding ethics*. Indianapolis, IN: Alpha.

Janis, I. L. (1983). *Groupthink: Psychological studies of policy in decisions and fiascoes* (2nd ed). Boston: Houghton Mifflin.

Johnson, W. B., & Ridley, C. R. (2008). *The elements of ethics*. New York: Palgrave MacMillan.

Kenny, A. (1994). Descartes to Kant. In A. Kenny (Ed.), *The Oxford illustrated history of Western philosophy* (pp. 107–192). New York: Oxford.

Kida, T. (2006). *Don't believe everything you think: The 6 basic mistakes we make in thinking.* Amherst, NY: Prometheus Books.

Kidder, R. (2003). *How good people make tough choices.* New York: Quill.

Kurland, D. J. (1995). *I know what it says . . . what does it mean?* Belmont, CA: Wadsworth.

Kurtz, P. (2007). What is the relationship among science, reason, and ethics? In P. Kurtz (Ed.), *Science and ethics: Can science help us make wise moral judgments?* (pp. 11–26). Amherst, NY: Prometheus Books.

Law, S. (2007). *Philosophy.* London: DK.

Levy, D. A. (1997). *Tools of critical thinking: Metathoughts for psychology.* Boston: Allyn & Bacon.

Lilienfeld, S. O. (2007). The assault on scientific mental health: Ethical implications. In P. Kurtz (Ed.), *Science and ethics: Can science help us make wise moral judgments* (pp. 207–224). Amherst, NY: Prometheus.

MacDonald, M. (2008). *Your brain: The missing manual.* Sebastopol, CA: O'Reilly Media.

MacKinnon, B. (2004). *Ethics: Theory and contemporary issues* (4th ed.). Belmont, CA: Wadsworth/Thomson.

Magee, B. (1998). *The story of philosophy.* London: DK Publishing.

Manuel, J. K., & Forcehimes, A. A. (2008). The therapeutic relationship in substance abuse treatment. In G. M. A. Geppert & L. W. Roberts (Eds.), *The book of ethics: Expert guidance for professionals who treat addiction* (pp. 29–39). Center City, MN: Hazelden.

Marcus, G. (2008). *Kluge.* Boston: Houghton Mifflin.

Marinoff, L. (2003). *The big questions: How philosophy can change your life.* New York: Bloomsbury.

Miller, G. (2005). *Learning the language of addiction counseling* (2nd Ed.). Hoboken, NJ: John Wiley & Sons.

Miller, W. (2008). The ethics of harm reduction. In C. M. A. Geppert & L. W. Roberts (Eds.), *The book of ethics: Expert guidance for professionals who treat addiction* (pp. 41–51). Center City, MN: Hazelden.

Miller, W., & Rollnick, S. (1991). *Motivational interviewing: Preparing people to change addictive behavior.* New York: Guilford.

Moore, B. N., & Parker, R. (1995). *Critical thinking* (4th ed.). Mountain View, CA: Mayfield.

NAADAC. (1994). Ethical standards of alcoholism and drug abuse counselors: Specific principles. *Counselor, 12*(3), 22–24.

Neukrug, E. (1999). *The world of the counselor: An introduction to the counseling profession.* Pacific Grove, CA: Brooks/Cole.

Paul, R. (1993). *Critical thinking.* Santa Rosa, CA: The Foundation for Critical Thinking.

Perkins, D. N. (2002). The engine of folly. In R. J. Sternberg (Ed.), *Why smart people can be so stupid* (pp. 64–85). New Haven, CT: Yale University Press.

Piattelli-Palmarini, M. (1994). *Inevitable illusions: How mistakes of reason rule our minds.* New York: Wiley.

Pinker, S. (2002). *The blank state: The modern denial of human nature.* New York: Viking.

Pizarro, D. (2000). Nothing more than feelings? The role of emotions in moral judgment. *Journal for the Theory of Social Behavior, 30*(4), 355–375.

Pope, K. S., & Vasquez, M. J. T. (2007). *Ethics in psychotherapy and counseling: A practical guide* (3rd ed.). San Francisco, CA: Jossey-Bass.

Rachels, J. (1986). *The elements of moral philosophy.* New York: McGraw-Hill.

Rauhut, N. C. (2006). *The big questions: Philosophy for everyone.* New York: Pearson Longman.

Ray, W. J. (2000). *Methods toward a science of behavior and experience.* Belmont, CA: Wadsworth/Thomson.

Riniolo, T. C. (2008). *When good thinking goes bad: How your brain can have a mind of its own.* Amherst, NY: Prometheus.

Roberson, D., & Garratt, C. (1999). *Introducing ethics.* Cambridge, UK: Icon Books.

Sagan, C. (1996). *The demon-haunted world: Science as a candle in the dark.* New York: Random House.

Shermer, M. (2004). *The science of good and evil.* New York: Times Books.

Singer, S. (2008, June 5). *Video shows bystanders ignorning hit-and-run victum.* Associated Press. Retrieved June 5, 2008, from http://blog.cleveland.com/pdextra/2008/06/video_shows_bystanders_ignorein.html

Solomon, R. C. (1993). *Ethics: A short introduction.* Dubuque, IA: Brown & Benchmark.

Solomon, R. C. (1999). *The joy of philosophy: Thinking thin versus that passionate life.* New York: Oxford University Press.

Steward, D., & Blocker, H. G. (1982). *Fundamentals of philosophy.* New York: McMillan.

St. Germaine, J. (1997). A national survey of state certification boards. *Alcoholism Treatment Quarterly, 15*(2), 63–72.

Strathern, P. (1996). *Kant in 90 minutes.* Chicago: Ivan R. Dee.

Taleff, M. J. (1997). *A handbook to assess and treat resistance in chemical dependency.* Dubuque, IA: Kendall/Hunt.

Taleff, M. J. (2005). Professional development. In R. H. Coombs (Ed.), *Addiction counseling review: Preparing for comprehensive, certification and licensing examinations* (pp. 557–576). Mahwah, NJ: Lawrence Erlbaum Associates.

Taleff, M. J. (2006). *Critical thinking for addiction professionals.* New York: Springer.

Tangney, J. P., Stueing, J., & Mashek, D. J. (2007). Moral emotions and moral behavior. *Annual Review of Psychology, 58,* 345–372.

Tannan, D. (1998). *The argument culture: Stopping America's war of words.* New York: Ballantine.

Tavris, C., & Aronson, E. (2007). *Mistakes were made, but not by me: Why we justify foolish beliefs, bad decision, and hurtful acts.* Orlando, FL: Harcourt.

Thompson, M. (2003). *Teach yourself ethics.* Chicago: Contemporary Press.

Thomson, A. (1999). *Critical reasoning in ethics.* London: Routledge.

Turnbull, N. (1998). *Get a grip on philosophy.* East Sussex, England: Ivy Press Limited.

Van Doren, C. (1991). *A history of knowledge: Past, present, and future.* New York: Ballantine.

Vaughn, L. (2008). *The power of critical thinking* (2nd ed.) New York: Oxford University Press.

Vivian, F. (1968). *Thinking philosophically: An introduction for students*. London: Chatto & Windus.

White, W. L. (2005). Professional ethics. In R. H. Coombs (Ed.), *Addiction counseling review: Preparing for comprehensive certification and licensing examinations* (pp. 535–555). Mahwah, NJ: Lawrence Erlbaum Associates.

Whyte, J. (2005). *Crimes against logic*. New York: McGraw-Hill.

Wolpert, L. (2006). *Six impossible things before breakfast*. New York: Norton.

Wright, R. (1994). *The moral animal*. New York: Vintage.

Woodhouse, M. B. (1994). *A preface of philosophy* (5th ed.). Belmont, CA: Wadsworth.

Youngson, R. (1998). *Scientific blunders: A brief history of how wrong scientists can be*. New York: Carroll & Graf.

Index